Price Guide to

ANTIQUE

Slot

MACHINES

Richard D. and Barbara Reddock

Library of Congress
Catalog Number 80-51976

ISBN 0-87069-332-8

Editors Note: The information and pictures contained
in this book cannot be used to solicit the sale of slot
machines in any jurisdiction where machines may not
be lawfully sold or operated.

Published by

Wallace-Homestead Book Company
1912 Grand Avenue
Des Moines, Iowa 50309

To My Wife Barbara

To my wife Barbara and to every wife who shares her husband's all-consuming passion and enthusiasm as a "slot machine collector"; who finds him discussing for hours his collection, visiting and viewing other collections, and many times, driving hundreds of miles in search of a machine or case which he does not have in his collection; for enduring the endless antique shows, miles of flea markets, letter writing, long distance phone calls and of course, the extravagant amounts of money spent on antique slot machines.

What collector's wife has not at one time or another asked "Is this worth it?" or "Is your slot machine collection all you care about?" It is no small measure then to acknowledge that without these companionable, patient, and understanding wives, slot machine collecting would not be all it is . . . for that we thank you wives!!!

. . . And to Mr. Marvin Leiter and Mr. Nicholas F. Cuneo, who as I watched over the slot machines, they watched over me . . . to them I am eternally grateful.

 # About This Book

This book will add another volume of insight to the fast growing area of collecting antique coin-operated machines and slot machines in particular. This relatively new collectible has caught the eye and imagination of many people. There is excitement in owning an antique slot machine; it covers a variety of emotions.

It is a part of American inventiveness and enterprise. From the early upright cabinet models to the familiar "one armed bandits," even to the modern electronic marvels, it's American all the way.

Those collectors who have an eye for the artistic side of design and craftsmanship can also have an affection for the early slot machines. The styles of the early wood cabinets to the ornate cast iron tooling of the early counter model slot machines leave one asking the question, where have the craftsmen gone? And, as with any intricate mechanical device, there are those people who love to "fiddle" with the mechanisms.

Another part of owning an antique slot machine is the attempt to beat the odds. Playing the slot and hoping for the reels to stop on a big winner is excitement for many people. So here we have a book that shows us only a portion of the antique slot machines made in this country. To make one to show all would be an almost impossible task. The number of models by the many manufacturers and their variations and the variations of the operators and distributors to satisfy the tastes of a nation are enormous.

This book and others, now and in the future, will give to the new collector a great insight into the fascinating field of antique coin-operated machine collecting. With the entrance of prestigious auction houses, such as Sotheby's, into selling of machines, this relatively new collecting fancy enters a new stage of enhancement. Each week new and unseen machines are found that excite the collectors with the hope of finding an unreported antique. This hobby is one that is expanding both in knowledge and in individuals who are looking for something that many other hobby areas cannot supply.

Melvin Getlan

 # Preface

This book lists one of the most extensive and complete collections of antique slot machines to date.

We believe that the prices for many of the antique slot machines in this book cannot be looked at as "high." Antique slot machines are similar to the stock market. If they are bringing high prices today, that is what they are worth. Three to five years ago they were bringing lower prices. There were just so many pieces made; hindsight is always 20/20 and one cannot go by the prices and values of yesterday. We have valued the items at today's current retail market value and have tried to take into consideration various price and cost comparisons throughout the country; however, there is no doubt that in different parts of the country and even in different parts of the same state prices can vary widely. We have based our values on items being in excellent to mint condition. When the condition of the machine decreases, so does the value.

The price increase in slot machine collectibles and, for that matter, any coin operated collectible, has skyrocketed. Where it will stop, as Ted Mack used to say, "no one knows." Certainly there must be a limit, but only time will tell. As long as there are collectors who are willing to pay for their hobby, the prices will continue to go up.

Some items have not been valued at this time. This is due to many factors, including the item's rarity or that collectors will not sell or trade it, or that it is manufactured only in a small section of the country, or was possibly used as an early promotion or sample that was never produced.

Correspondence from fellow antique slot machine collectors is invited. Information about any item is available. We would appreciate the notification and photograph of the existence of any items not listed herein. Write to us at: Reddock, P.O. Box 524, North Bellmore, New York 11710.

Thank you,
Richard D. and Barbara Reddock

 # Acknowledgments

The authors wish to express their gratitude to the many individuals mentioned below who have supplied us information or understanding and have given generously of their time to make this volume possible.

Dr. Ron and Randee Stern
Dr. Jeffrey and Sandy Lubin
Sy and Lorraine Mautner
Thomas S. Gulotta
(Assemblyman, New York State)
Lawrence T. Schimel
Marvin Moelis
Morty Held
Sy Rosenthal
Robert Sterling
Ray Dirks
Jeff and Sharon Halper
Robert and Phyllis Popkin
Linda Lander
Irving and Selma Goodman
Rudy and Cookie Farano
Gloria Weinstock
Arthur and Bea Goodman
Paul and Sue Gordon
Tom Heffernan
Nelson Schneider
Fred Shwom
Doug Lynn

Jay Grossman
Guy Ball
Hy Aronow
John Labanowski
Charles Farb
Linda Rhodes
Gladys Lawson
Danny Liebowitz
Larry and Pat Cohen
Julie and Florence Cohen
Bob McGraph, Jr.
Charles Saluda
Lena Lane
Ian Reddock
Jill Beth Reddock
Neil and Rachelle Singer
Jerry Rosen
Tony Mills
Mel Bernstein
Al and Ann Menaker
Tulsi Reynolds
Dr. Richard and Marian Salerno

The authors wish to express their special thanks for the help they received from **Bally Manufacturing Corporation** and their people.

Chicago
Ross B. Scheen, Director of Marketing
Carol Mart Porth, Promotion Manager
Mr. Herb Jones

Atlantic City
Richard Gillman, Chairman of the Board, Bally Park Place Hotel and Casino
William S. Weinberger, President, Bally Park Place Casino
Lucille Cohen
Rita Shade
Helen McHugh

Boston
Arnold A. Kaminkow, President, Bally Northeast
Robert T. Mahony, Sales Manager, Bally Northeast
Janie Feldman

Reno, Nevada
Alan Maiss, Formerly Vice President, Bally Distributing Company, Presently Corporate Vice President of Horn and Hardart Company and President of Royal Center, Inc., Royal Americana Hotel and Casino, Las Vegas, Nevada

Some beautiful people — without their efforts this book may never have been produced.

Barbara Lee Gardella	*Julie Collier*
Pamela Brown	*Christie's East*
Pamela Fraleigh	*Lynn and Allen Adler*
Melvin Getlan	
Collectibles Department, Sotheby's	*Arnold A. Kaminkow*
Phil Metzger	

Special Thanks To:

Alan and Helene Luchnick
Back Pages Antiques

Charles and Claire McCann

Gil Shapiro
Urban Archaeology

Tom Krahl

Joel Gilgoff
G.A.M.E.S.

Howard Schwartz
Gambler's Book Club

Gordon Pace
Pace Auctions

Roy Arrington
Victorian Casino
    Antiques Auction

Bill and Rosanna Harris
Coin Slot Books

Richard J. Jubanyik, Esq.
Jubanyik, Uarbalow, Tedesco and Shaw

Vinnie Dobos
Vintage Machine Sales

Ed and Jan Stevens
Michael Levin
Virgil Vance
Pete Hansen
Ira Warren
Gary H. Moise
Irwin and Rita Shapiro
Paul Galant
Ron and Leslie Brodis
Bonnie Tekstra
Brian Longley
Bob Lan Franco
Barry Klein

Photographers
Glenn Ellman
Gregg Ellman
Al Tepe
Ian Reddock

Robert Marcus

Al and Phyllis Freiberger
Barry Rubenstein
Mike DeBenedetto
Fred Dolin
Herb Stone
Herman Finesod
United Press International, Inc.
Wide World Photos
Larry Polans

The Good Guys
Marvin B. Segal
Robert L. Beerman
Phil Smith
Malan Frankhauser
Jim Druker

 # Contents

🔔 Introduction

Richard D. and Barbara Reddock approached me to write an introduction for this book, and admittedly this writer was at a loss for words. However, that was only a brief state of things. As an editor of a magazine one cannot afford to be at a loss for words for long.

The hobby of collecting antique slot machines has been around for years. Essentially it cannot be dated because until recently it was illegal to own or possess a slot machine except in Nevada. Many people did, in fact, own slot machines after the crackdown under the Johnson Act in 1951. For the most part the machines were hidden (some very carefully and others not so carefully). Perhaps this was the springboard for the hobby of collecting machines.

In the early years there were few collectors and few dealers. Machines seemed to be scarce and there were limited numbers of them that showed up for sale, normally surrounded by clandestine meetings in deserted parking lots or a dark room in the back of a shop. There was an aura of mystery and intrigue which heightened the adventure of owning the famed "one-armed bandits." But it was not an area for the faint-hearted collector. It was one thing to collect guns or advertising memorabilia, but quite another to collect machines which at any given time could produce a raid by the local police or agents of the F.B.I.

The original collectors and dealers took advantage of the working, more choice machines. The collectibility of the machines continued to grow and spread and the numbers in both ranks — collectors and dealers — also grew. Eventually the dealers returned to some of their sources and salvaged the non-working machines from the chicken coops, barns, basements, and closets where they had rested for years. Both the dealers and collectors quickly realized that information was sorely needed.

A quiet movement began with a newsletter called "The Coin Slot" from New York. Names slowly were added to the mailing list, and the small group of people commenced exchanging any and all information which they had accumulated in these early years of collecting. As the readership grew

the people banded together and began movements to change the laws regarding slot machines and trade stimulators in their respective states. What started as a small handful of special interest people mushroomed into a large group interested in machines, arcade pieces, and assorted related paraphernalia.

*Coin Slot Books published its first major book, **An Illustrated Price Guide to the 100 Most Collectible Slot Machines,** in 1978. Then followed three more books — Volume II on slot machines, and two on trade stimulators. A series of guides for individual machines or related groups of machines was written by Richard M. Bueschel, also the author of the other four. Other authors and publishing firms have added even more information to the field. This book, written by Richard D. and Barbara Reddock, offers still another dimension to the hobby of collecting antique coin-operated devices.*

Today's collector is in a position to enjoy his machines even more because of the labor of love of all these authors and publishers. Our compliments and deep-felt appreciation to Richard and Barbara for this latest addition to one of the most exciting hobbies of collecting.

Rosanna Harris, Editor
"The Coin Slot"

1. Collecting Antique Slot Machines

We as Americans are a very unique people! We are always looking to the future, to new frontiers. Ours is a country with creative people so energetic that sometimes along the way we don't stop "to smell the flowers." Only until years later do we appreciate what we had!

In the mood for just simple relaxation, this afternoon, I watched an old 1930s Laurel and Hardy movie. The title escapes me, but it was set in a gold mining town out West in the early 1900s. This rather hazy print, almost 50 years old, was more than just an hour or two of laughs. I was fascinated by all those fixtures used at that time: rooms full of oak furniture, beveled mirror, brass beds, Tiffany lamps, oak back bars. And what about all those slot machines; early oak uprights, like the Mills Dewey and the Caille Brothers Black Cat. All around were fabulous modes of the Owl, Buffalo, Lion, and one or two Duplex uprights. I would not only love to own every slot machine in that movie but each and every piece of equipment used in the film. Today these same props are very much sought after by collectors, yet back in the 1930s when this movie was made these items were simple stage props that could have been purchased by anyone.

Does this mean that in 20 or 30 years from now my children, Ian who is 13, and Jill who is 11, will consider a McDonalds doll, Burger King Star Wars glass, or a plastic Coke® bottle a find, or that in their gameroom will be an "Antique Bally Space Invaders Machine"? Who can say? Although we still use coins in our everyday life, in many coin-operated devices the computer and the plastic card are hard on its heels. It is times like these that one really appreciates the slot-machines and other coin-operated machines of years gone by. Those of you who are lucky enough to own some of these machines know what I mean. Others of you who are seeing these machines for the first time in this book, or who never knew the scope of machines available, I can only wish you the joy of the hunt, enjoyment of ownership, and a wise investment for antique slot machines and these other coin operated devices; all of this and more.

Today the following names: Mills, Frey, Jennings, Pace, Watling, Caille, and others, are gone from the screen. The coin-operated business is now a multi-billion dollar industry and the slot machine business is dominated by companies like Bally Manufacturing Corporation. The days of the individual inventor, tinker, or just plain entrepreneur who wanted to make a slot machine are gone forever, replaced by research groups, accountants, computer people, and boards of directors! All we have left of those days are beautiful pieces of American machines, art at its best! Put in your coin, pull the handle, watch the reels turn, and hope when they stop you are a winner. To my way of thinking anyone who owns one of these machines is already a winner.

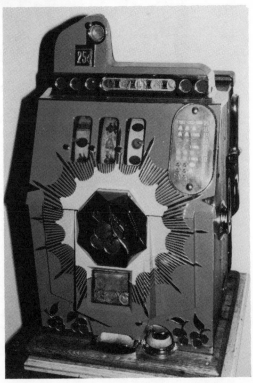

🔔 Slot Machine Prices What Determines Them?

The slot machines shown in this Wallace-Homestead Price Guide To Antique Slot Machines are in fine to excellent condition and are priced accordingly. As with the other book we did, *Planters Peanuts Advertising & Collectibles* with current prices, we have learned that many people were unhappy with the prices. Some think the prices are too high, some too low, but most feel they are fair. Mostly it is some dealers who got upset. One must remember that it takes almost a year to get a book ready and prices do change. Also, the "Planters" book is in its second printing and the prices were never changed.

Anyone who purchases this book can write to us for information and/or updated prices. There is a coupon in the back of the book good for a free copy of "Slot Machine Newsletter" which will update prices and keep you abreast of what is happening in the field.

In the following "Guide to Grading" I will attempt to clear up some questions you may have. Remember, a slot machine is really two separate parts, the case and the mechanism.

A Guide To Grading

Special Rare Class:
Slot machines falling into this class are usually very early models, with few remaining examples, and are in mint, i.e. still in their original crate or perfectly restored.

Mint-Mint Condition:
This is what most people think of as mint. Not in its original mint condition, very minor or slight marks of age or usage, or a complete, professionally restored slot machine.

Excellent Condition:
Only minor wear on cabinet or mechanism; all original parts must be there.

Very Good Condition:
Minor surface wear on cabinet and mechanism; some restoration acceptable; no rust and all original parts.

Good Condition:
This is the slot machine that most of you will come across. There are some minor cabinet scratches, dents, nicks, pits, fading, little rust. All major original parts are there, some small parts may be missing or changed or machine may have been restored, but not in the highest professional manner. Payout must be correct.

Fair Condition:
Major surface scratches, minor dents, paint fading, some rust or pitting. Machine has been used and is dirty, wear is very evident. Recast parts may be needed and some cracks may have to be filled and repaired. Back door usually not original.

Poor Condition:
Badly chipped, dirty, rusted, worn, dented, and so on. Parts missing, cracks, machine may not work, missing glass. With care and skill can be put back into shape, but is it worth it?

Unacceptable Condition:
A basket case, major parts missing, incomplete.

Purchase of First Slot Machine at Christie's East

On Tuesday, November 25, 1980 at 6:30 p.m., the auctioneer mounted the rostrum to start the first American Casino Collectibles Auction of antique slot machines, trade stimulators, vending machines, and other coin operated devices. My wife, Barbara, and I were determined to purchase the very first lot that went up at auction and hoped that Christie's would make it a reasonable item, so we could go down in history as purchasing the very first slot machine at this famous auction house. We opened the auction catalog looking to see what lot #1 was. We were both happy and surprised; it read:

> 1. *A MILLS "HIGH TOP" 10¢ 3-REEL SLOT MACHINE CASE, partially done-in by a member of Mayor Fiorello LaGuardia's Vice Squad. Height 19", late 1930s, unrestored.*
> *Estimate $50-75*

Since we were writing our book on antique slot machines and Christie's chose to start off the auction with a little humor, it was just perfect for us. We went up to look at the battered machine, behind the rostrum. Tables were set up with hundreds of slot machines all lined up like soldiers ready to be sold. As we scanned the tables looking for No. 1, I noticed a friend of mine, Pete Hansen, a dealer from the midwest, looking at a machine. Sure enough it was No. 1, a very battered red High-Top, no top, no mechanism, no back door, and definitely done-in by someone's sledge hammer, many years ago. Pete was looking over the machine for parts, ten dollars for this part, twenty dollars for the change cup, maybe five dollars for the handle. Pete came up with "It's worth forty dollars in parts." I said to him, "I need this machine for my book!"

"We'll see," said Pete, as he walked away. Barbara and I looked at the machine. "It has personality," Barbara said as we walked away.

At the stroke of 6:30 p.m., the auction started. As the boys held up the battered High-Top machine for all to see, the audience laughed. The auctioneer said, "Who will start this off at $25.00." I immediately raised my numbered bidding paddle. "$25.00 we have," said the auctioneer, looking around for another bid. "$40,00," a voice calls as a hand stabs the air. I looked for the raised hand, which was a few rows in front of us, and I saw it belonged to Pete Hansen. "$50.00," I yelled out with authority.

"SOLD," said the auctioneer as he tapped down the wood to close the sale. "Yours at $50.00." I smiled, I was happy . . . as the auctioneer went on to the next lot I saw Pete turn around to see who purchased lot No. 1. He smiled at me and I smiled back. I know that I can always sell it to Pete Hansen for $40.00, but will he pay shipping??

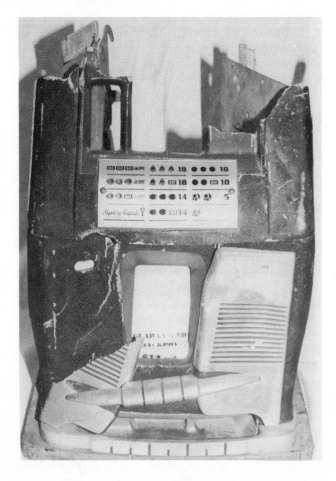

First Slot Machine Auctioned at Christie's East
No. 1—A MILLS "HIGH-TOP" 10¢ 3-REEL SLOT MACHINE CASE, partially done-in by a member of Mayor Fiorello LaGuardia's Vice Squad. Height 19", late 1930s, unrestored.   *Estimate $50–75*

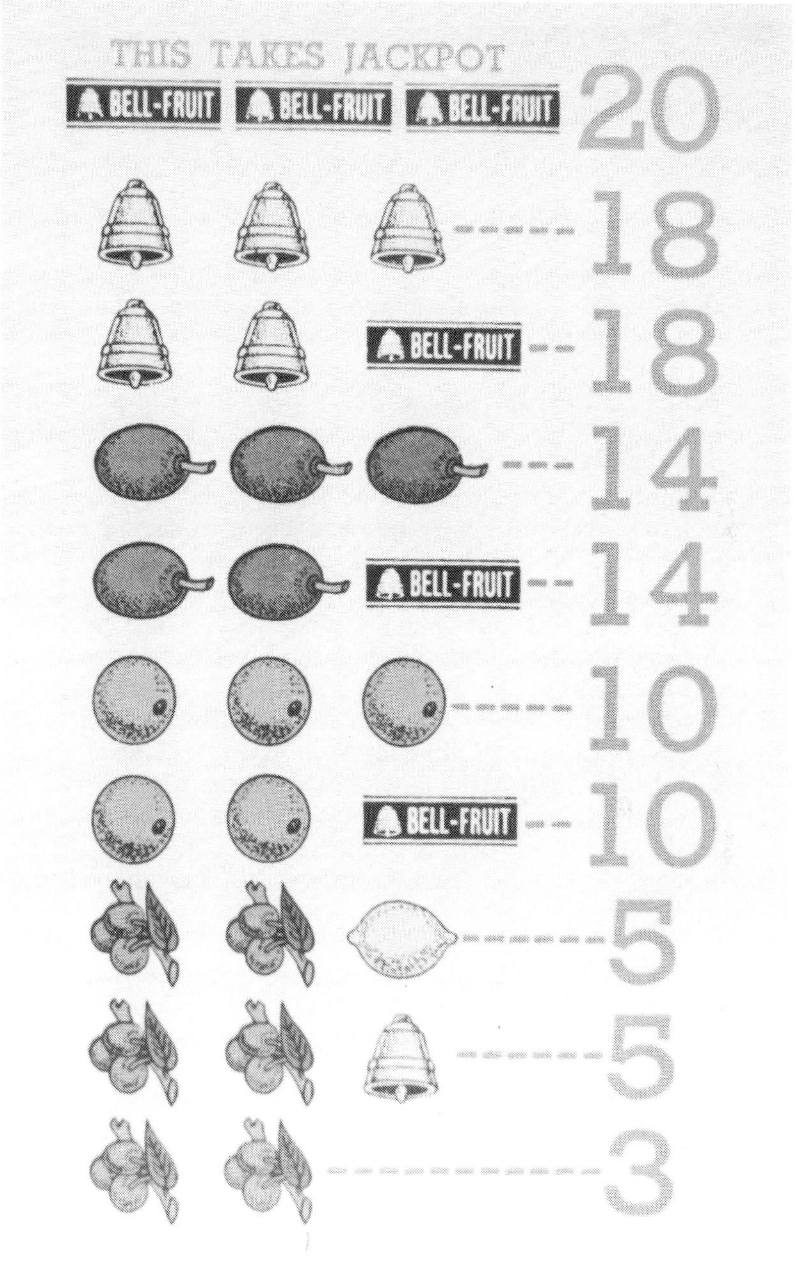

BELL-FRUIT BELL-FRUIT BELL-FRUIT 20

18

BELL-FRUIT 18

14

BELL-FRUIT 14

10

BELL-FRUIT 10

5

5

3

♠ Some
Slot Machine History

The slot machine, as we have come to know it, is credited as being the brainchild of a Bavarian immigrant, Charles Fey. Fey, born in 1862, immigrated to the United States in 1882. Arriving in San Francisco, California in 1887, he worked as a mechanic for an electrical supply company. In his spare time, Fey devoted himself to his inventions and innovative projects. It was during this period that Fey developed what is affectionately called the "grand daddy" of all slot machines, the Liberty Bell slot machine. The Liberty Bell was introduced in 1905.

Up until this time coin-operated games of chance were really nothing new. Several companies had been producing several various types in previous years. Some were based on such games as roulette, dice, cards, and horse-racing. Others were based on numbers or colors. While some machines used a single revolving disc, or wheel, others employed the use of reels similar to those used by Fey. Most early machines were quite heavy and bulky, most being console designs. Although these early machines were somewhat amusing and minimally exciting, they never attained the height of popularity the latter slot machines were to have.

Fey, who had been making coin machines some years before developing the Liberty Bell, is considered to be the father of the slot machine industry. The Liberty Bell slot machine was the first three reel slot to feature automatic cash payouts. It was NOT, however, the first three reel machine ever made. Fey's Liberty Bell was a comparatively compact machine, lighter in weight than most coin-operated machines of the period, and the automatic payout attracted more player action. Originally designed for use by patrons of the local saloons in and around the Bay area, the Liberty Bell's reward plate appropriately listed the payoffs in drinks rather than in coins, although the machine did, in fact, pay out in nickels.

Payment of rewards was accomplished by use of three closely positioned plates, perforated in designated places to correspond to the symbols, which spun in conjunction with the three reels. Upon lining up a winning combination, certain perforations are aligned, allowing "fingers" within the machine to protrude

through them. This causes another mechanism, called a "coin-slide," to be activated, and a predetermined number of coins is caused to be dispensed into the money bowl for the lucky player to pick up. Different perforations, strategically located, make possible the different payouts in compliance with the posted pay-off rates for winning combinations. The whole event is based on the random process, which means that nothing compels the reels to stop at any pre-determined point. Each spin of the reels is an independent process, and players could not determine when the reels would stop on a winning combination. Since nothing compels the reels to stop on a winning combination OR a losing combination, predictability is out. The players were gambling.

Fey's Liberty Bell uses 10 symbols on each reel. This means that there are 1,000 possible combinations that can appear in the window ($10 \times 10 \times 10 = 1,000$). Since the reels spin around randomly, it is virtually impossible to outguess the outcome. Players were really getting their money's worth in action and suspense.

Fey, refusing to sell his machine, placed them in businesses on a share-profit basis, fifty percent of the "take" to the proprietor and fifty percent to Fey. Fey personally conducted the business of leasing and collecting, travelling by horse and buggy. This limited his coverage since it was impossible to travel great distances. Therefore, his machines were limited to the Bay area, although he did extend his business in later years to include some central California areas, too.

Since some of the symbols on the original Liberty Bell were representative of playing card symbols (hearts, diamonds, etc.), Fey put a 2¢ Federal Revenue Stamp on each machine.

Since gambling devices aren't patentable, Fey's only protection was to:
1. Refuse sale of the machines
2. Restrict their distribution to a limited area
3. Personally supervise the over-all operation

It is obvious that Fey wanted to keep utmost control of his machines and business; however, competition was imminent. Others in the coin operated machine business learned of Fey's Liberty Bell and of the success it was having. One such person was Herbert Stephen Mills, who had been in the coin operated machine business several years prior to Fey. Mills, well established in the industry, was determined to acquire one of Fey's machines. Mills somehow acquired one of the machines, and after much redesigning and modifying, in 1909 presented the Mills Liberty Bell slot machine.

Mills' Liberty Bell uses basically the same symbols Fey used with the addition of the jack, queen, king symbols. This machine is larger than Fey's machine, and was reengineered to make the over-all operation smoother and more durable. The Mills machine is a direct steal from Fey, just slightly modified here and there. Mills also added 10 more symbols to each of his reels. This made 8,000 possible combinations that could appear on the pay-line (20 $\times$ 20 $\times$ 20 = 8,000). Mills widened the window on his machines so the player could now see three rows of symbols (a total of nine symbols at once). By adding more symbols, more winning combinations could be created and posted on the reward plate, including play. Also, more losing combinations were possible, mathematically, and therefore the machines' earning power increased.

Mills produced another version of this machine in 1910, calling it the Operator's Bell. It is essentially the same machine as the Mills Liberty Bell, except that the reel symbols are bells, bars, cherries, etc., and the card symbols are deleted. It was widely received by operators throughout the country.

About the same time as Mills was producing his Liberty Bell machines, another company followed with a similar version. Caille Brothers Co., who had been in the coin machine business for several years, copied Mills' machine and, in 1910, introduced the Caille Liberty Bell slot machine.

Both Mills and Caille Brothers produced their slot machines while Charles Fey continued to develop and build his machines in the usual manner in San Francisco. Fey's last machine was a silver dollar slot produced in 1929.

The new trend in slot design established by Fey and eagerly copied by Mills, Caille Brothers, and others, became increasingly noticeable throughout the nation as more machines by more and more producers flooded the market. The console models slowly went by the wayside as the new style counter-top models came into vogue. Some console machines were still being produced on into the 1930s, but their diminishing popularity was evident with the ever increasing numbers of new 3-reelers dominating the markets.

Preference to the new 3-reelers was partly due to their size and weight. While console models were floor models standing as high as 63 inches or more, and weighing from 200 to 500 pounds or more, portability and space were two criteria solved by the 3-reel counter-top machines.

It is easy to understand why the new 3-reelers were preferred over console models. A wider selection of counter models was available. More machines could be placed in an establishment in less space. More income could be generated as more players could be attracted, and the machines could be moved more easily should the need arise. The new 3-reelers weighed anywhere from 70+ to 100+ pounds, depending on the model, which was quite a contrast to the heavier consoles.

Although Mills held the lead in slot production, competition was growing. Some companies produced slots as a sideline, others as a sole product. For the next several years the slot industry flourished with such names as Caille Brothers, Synder, Daval, Groetchen, C & F Mfg., Rock-ola, Southern Doll Mfg., Pierce, Burtmeier, Skelly, Pace, Baker, Watling, Keeney, Buckley, Evans, and several other, but lesser known, companies. In more recent years such names as Bally, Seeburg, Jennings and others have dominated the market. Many of the early machines are now prized and valuable collector's items.

As legal problems concerning gambling arose throughout the country during the 30s and 40s, slot manufacturers realized that something had to be done to at least make slot playing appear legally justifiable. In order to stay in business slot manufacturers attempted to dodge legal obstacles and appease moralists at the same time by producing machines with vending devices and attachments built into the machines. Under the guise of merchandising, the vending devices were filled with candy or gum and a player was able to get something for playing, while still standing a chance of winning a coin or two. In some areas this "merchandising" scheme worked. Vending models were among the most elaborate and ornately designed slot machines ever produced. They were manufactured well into the 1930s. Although the vending idea faded, several models were produced and comprised the most colorful chapter in the history of slot machines.

THE JACKPOT. Although the jackpot was featured in consoles pre-dating Fey's Liberty Bell, it wasn't until 1916 that the jackpot was tried on a 3-reel counter-top model. First tried in an experimental version of a re-cast 1915 Mills Operator's Bell machine by Watling Mfg., the jackpot assembly consisted of a container and a trap door. Hand-filled by the operator, the coins were visible to the player through a window in front of the container. The exact number of coins was undeterminable to the player. Upon lining up the qualifying jackpot symbols on the

pay-line, a pre-determined amount of coins was automatically paid by the machine and, simultaneously, the trap door of the container was released, allowing the container's contents to also drop into the money bowl. The term "drop" jackpot is derived from this method of pay. For some reason the drop jackpot idea failed. Watling Mfg. tried it again in 1920 with the introduction of a machine called the O.K. Jackpot. Again, the jackpot idea failed to gain success.

Mills incorporated the jackpot into his machines in 1925, nine years later, and it became an immediate success. Perhaps timing was the key factor. Soon after it appeared, every other slot manufacturer started incorporating the jackpot into their machines. From then on the jackpot became an integral feature.

Since the drop jackpot containers were only partially filled with coins by the operators themselves, and sometimes thereafter by player action as coins were played into the machines, a variable between jackpot values existed. Although a predetermined amount was automatically paid by some machines upon lining up a jackpot combination, with the container's contents added as a bonus, there was no way to determine a jackpot's exact value until it was won and counted.

Legalized gambling was introduced to Nevada in 1931, and new state regulations prohibited the variable and indeterminable jackpots delivered by the drop jackpot method. The new laws made three provisions concerning slot machine jackpots:

1. Jackpots must be of a specific value
2. This value must be conspicuously advertised (displayed) on each machine
3. Jackpots, as well as all other awards posted, must be attainable and payable in full if won

These provisions also applied to all awards . . . and still do.

Slot manufacturers, eager to cash in on the booming Nevada gambling industry, quickly modified their machines to comply with the new laws of Nevada. These laws still apply and are enforced.

With legalized gambling and slot regulations firmly established in Nevada, slot manufacturers were now facing other problems elsewhere in the nation. In the early 1930s and continuing into the 1940s, a national move was underway to make slots illegal, except in counties and states that still wanted to legally permit them. This problem was enhanced when, in 1950, the federal government passed a law making it illegal to ship machines across state lines, except into those areas where they were still legal.

As fewer and fewer states and counties permitted them, the market for slot machines naturally decreased, causing many early manufacturers to cease slot production. Although several foreign markets were still open, Nevada was the primary American market, with only a sprinkling of a few other legally authorized areas in other states. Since most slot manufacturers were based in Chicago, many closed their doors or pursued other product lines when Illinois passed the Johnson Act, a law prohibiting all out of state shipments of slots. Those that could moved to Nevada or Maryland where slots were still legal. This was the period Mills and Jennings became the world leaders in slot production and sales.

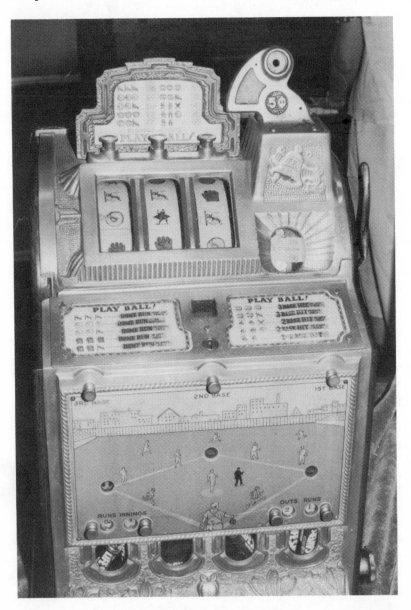

In 1963, the anti-slot machine laws were amended and manufacturers could resume production and out of state shipping. Prior to these anti-slot machine years there were only four major producers of slots: Jennings, Mills, Watling, and Pace. Pace folded in 1951. Watling sold the rights to its slots to a European concern. Mills' machines were being manufactured in Nevada, England, and Asia. Jennings became the leader and continued to manufacture on into the 1960s. TJM Corp. took over the Mills and Jennings machines and, in 1979, was in turn acquired by OTX Inc. Other slot manufacturers have also come into being since the 1960s.

Up until 1963, most slots were of the same basic design as they had been. Although lights had been added to make the machines more attractive, little was done to the basic mechanical aspects. Surely many changes had occurred over the years, but sophistication of the slot machine was still a little ways away.

1963, the year the anti-slot machine laws were amended, was to become the beginning of a new era in slot technology.

Bally Mfg., who began in 1931 as a manufacturer of pinball games, entered the realm of gambling with the addition of an automatic payout mechanism to one of its pinball machines in 1933. Bally produced their first slot machine in 1937 with the introduction of the Bally Double Bell. It never attained popularity. From 1941-48, Bally produced several console model slot machines in both pay and non-pay models. Bally withdrew from slot manufacture when restrictive laws went into effect. Bally, like so many others, concentrated on other product lines.

With new laws in effect, Bally re-entered the slot manufacturing industry in 1964 with the introduction of a radical new design in slot machines. The machine was called Money Honey.

Almost overnight Bally became the new leader in slot manufacturing. Money Honey was the most sophisticated and technologically advanced slot machine in the world and became the pacesetter in the field. What Fey's humble Liberty Bell was in 1905, the new Bally Money Honey machine became in 1964. There was no doubt about it. A new era was born.

2. How to Play for Fun and Profit

In the old days there was little to know in order to play a slot machine. One simply dropped a coin in the slot and pulled the handle. Either they won or lost. Today it isn't quite so simple. With multiple win lines, progressive jackpots, and larger jackpots available, a player just can't afford to miss out on a big win through negligence. But it happens everyday to someone. Many players are totally unaware of the variables existing between machines. Let's face it: Slot machines aren't what they used to be. They are a far cry from the single coin single pay-line machines of yesteryear. Today's machines may take from one to 15 coins at a time before pulling the handle. They may have one to five pay-lines. They may have from three to five reels.

As a rule it is recommended that the maximum amount of coins be played in order to qualify for a machine's highest award. If a machine takes three coins it will state so somewhere on the machine. The same goes for any type machine taking more than one coin. Some machines pay on more than one line, each line being qualified as a win-line when additional coins are inserted into the slot.

We will examine various models in order to show the difference and what to look for.

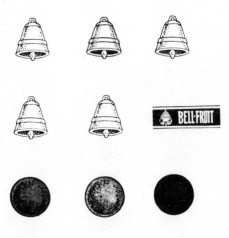

First of all, let's look at the most basic part . . . the pay-line. There are three basic pay-line versions:

1. *SINGLE-LINE PAY*
   Only the central horizontal row of symbols qualifies as the win line.

2. *THREE-LINE PAY*
   a. The first, or central, horizontal row of symbols qualifies as the win line when one coin is played prior to pulling the handle.

   b. The first and top horizontal rows of symbols qualify as win lines when two coins are inserted prior to pulling the handle.

   c. The center, top, and bottom horizontal rows of symbols qualify as win lines when three coins are inserted prior to pulling the handle.

3. *FIVE-LINE PAY*
   a. The first, or central, horizontal row of symbols qualifies as the win line when one coin is inserted prior to pulling the handle.

   b. The first and top horizontal rows of symbols qualify as win lines when two coins are inserted prior to pulling the handle.

   c. The center, top, and bottom horizontal rows of symbols qualify as win lines when three coins are inserted prior to pulling the handle.

   d. When a fourth coin is inserted prior to pulling the handle the symbols from top left to bottom right diagonally also qualify as a win line.

   e. When a fifth coin is inserted prior to pulling the handle, the symbols from bottom left to top right diagonally also qualify as a win line.

In all cases, whether the machine has one, three, or five pay lines, the maximum wins are only attainable when the maximum number of coins allowed is played into the machine prior to pulling the handle.

Now let's look at other variations of machines.

1. SINGLE-LINE PAY

a. Some single-line pay machines require only a single coin in order to win the machine's highest posted award, as well as all other awards.

b. Some require a minimum of one coin and a maximum of two. All payouts, including jackpots, are doubled when two coins are played.

c. Multipliers may be played with a single coin or as many as five or six coins. Wins are multiplied by the number of coins inserted prior to pulling the handle.

d. Some single-line pay machines not only pay from left to right, but also from right to left, upon lining up a winning combination of symbols.

e. Some multipliers may also have a bonus jackpot award amounting to hundreds and even many thousands of dollars should the qualifying jackpot symbols appear when the maximum number of coins allowed is played.

f. Progressive jackpots, increasing in value as coins are played into the machine, may also be found.

g. Some machines offer two progressive jackpots. Only one progressive jackpot is attainable and a red arrow will light up to indicate which jackpot is qualified when the maximum number of coins is played. The arrows light up alternatively.

h. Machines with more than three reels can also be found in single-pay line models.

i. Sometimes a machine may pay out "mystery" bonuses as a gimmick.

2. THREE-LINE PAY

a. As previously mentioned, each coin played qualifies a different win line.

b. On most machines the wins are not multiplied by the number of coins played prior to pulling the handle, only the number of win lines is increased.

c. One type of three-line pay machine, although not commonly found, does accept more than three coins. In effect the machine is just a multiplier version of a three-line pay machine.

d. Progressive jackpots are sometimes found on three-line pay machines. Whether the machine has one or two progressive jackpots, only the third line qualifies the player for it when the maximum number of coins is played prior to pulling the handle.

3. FIVE-LINE PAY

a. Each coin played into the machine prior to pulling the handle qualifies a different win line. Machine may be played with a minimum of one coin (qualifying the central horizontal row of symbols as the win line), or a maximum of five coins, qualifying all lines (three horizontal and two diagonal), as win lines.

b. Wins are not multiplied by number of coins played, only the number of win lines is increased.

c. Some five-line pay machines feature a progressive jackpot which increases in value as coins are played into the machine. Sometimes two progressive jackpots (as described previously in section 1. g.), are featured.

d. In all cases, the machine's highest awards are attainable only when the maximum number of coins allowed is played prior to pulling the handle.

It is obvious that there are several versions of slots available to the player.

In order to expose himself to the maximum wins offered on any machine a player must deposit the maximum number of coins allowed by that machine prior to pulling the handle and hope that the lucky combinations of symbols appear on the pay-line(s). Literally millions of dollars in jackpots and other awards are lost each year by aggregate players failing to insert the proper number of coins prior to pulling the handle. Part of the reason is due to negligence, and partly through ignorance. Now you know better.

You still have to get lucky, but why take extra risks? Play to win. In answer to the question of how to win: Use good judgment. Use good money management sense. Learn to read any and all information posted on the machine, and be sure you understand it, prior to inserting any coins. When playing progressive jackpot machines always choose machines with the highest value displayed. If you are a careful shopper and lucky enough gambler you will fare better than those who jump from one machine to another hoping to hit something in between.

# Know Your Percentage

Many players fall prey to the belief that a machine that hasn't produced any wins over a long period of time is becoming "due" to hit. Unfortunately, this just isn't true. The chances of a win do not increase with every pull, nor is the machine set to pay after a certain number of coins is played into it. It's all a matter of chance based on the random process.

Before getting into percentages let's look at the possible combinations of symbols that can appear on the pay-line(s). Since some reels have blank spaces where no symbol appears, machines are commonly referred to as being a 20 stop machine, or a 22 stop machine, etc. By multiplying the number of stops on reel 1 × reel 2 × reel 3 we can determine the number of combinations of stops that can appear on the center line (or any pay line), of that machine. If a machine has three reels, each reel will have an equal number of stops. The same applies to machines with four or five or more reels. Most machines will have reels with as few as 20 stops per reel, or 22 stops per reel, and 25 stops per reel. Very rarely will a machine exceed this number of stops.

Three Reel Slot

Reel One	×	Reel Two	×	Reel Three	=	Total Pay-Line Combinations
20	×	20	×	20	=	8,000
22	×	22	×	22	=	10,648
25	×	25	×	25	=	15,625

Four Reel Slot

Reel One	×	Reel Two	×	Reel Three	×	Reel Four	=	Total Pay-Line Combinations
20	×	20	×	20	×	20	=	160,000
22	×	22	×	22	×	22	=	234,256
25	×	25	×	25	×	25	=	390,625

On a five reel machine we simply multiply a fifth time.

In order to determine a machine's percentage it is necessary to learn the composition of the reel symbols on each reel. Once known it would be possible to find subgroups of winning combinations and compute the machine's percentage and know exactly what the player's true odds of winning are. It is not uncommon to have two or three or more identically appearing machines right next to each other, each drastically different in reel composition and overall percentage. Never assume that all machines are alike.

Here we see a percentage sheet (which is the actual paperwork of an existing machine somewhere), depicting not only the reel composition, but also the machine's percentage "hold."

BALLY CLASSIC

Model No. DC 616 (1148-3) Percentage 89.09%	Date 8-15-78
Machine name Classic (5 Coin Jillions Mult.)	Hold % 10.91

Symbols			1	2	3	Hits	Pay	Total	%
ME	ME	ME	8	8	9	576	20	11520	
BA	BA	BA	2	5	2	20	100	2000	
SE	SE	SE	1	1	1	1	200	200	

Total (1 Thru 4 Coins) 597	13720	87.81
SE SE SE (Aug. Bonus 5th Coin)	200	1.28
Total (5 Coins Played) 597	13920	89.09

Melon	8	8	9
Bar	2	5	2
Seven	1	1	1
Blanks	14	11	13
	25	25	25

Reel Tapes

1	2	3	
		ME	1
ME	ME		2
		ME	3
ME	BA		4
		BA	5
BA	ME		6
		ME	7
ME	ME		8
		ME	9
	BA		10
ME	ME	ME	11
			12
SE	SE	SE	13
	BA		14
			15
ME	ME	ME	16
			17
ME	ME	ME	18
			19
BA	BA	BA	20
			21
ME	ME	ME	22
	BA		23
ME		ME	24
	ME		25

The machine's percentage calculations are based on a theoretical spin of 15,625 plays with all possible combinations appearing in accordance to mathematical probability with all possible wins paid out.

Since machines do not have a "memory" of what has or hasn't happened, there will be times when a machine will perform differently than the mathematical formula dictates. There may be times when a machine fails to deliver any wins over a seemingly reasonable period of time (usually 6–12 plays, depending on the type of machine), and periods when a machine pays out more than an expected average of small and large wins. It is all a matter of random happenstance which adds to the excitement of play. Overall, each machine can be expected to adhere to its mathematical formula as dictated in its own paperwork. Each machine, when ordered from the factory, has its own paperwork. It is possible to have 30 identical machines, each with different numerical arrangements of symbols, to give 30 completely different percentages while still offering the same value awards.

 # You and the Law

As one who is a slot machine collector or who may be a potential owner of a slot machine you must become aware of the law in your state. As of December, 1980 thirty states have passed laws with reference to owning slot machines. Many other state laws are in the process of being changed, but as a free American you must vote to get the laws of your state changed. What this country really needs is a federal law making these antique slot machines legal. After all these machines are really America at its finest, and why should someone in California or New York be able to own one and someone who lives in Kentucky or Georgia not? It just does not make any sense. These machines are not really suited for gambling use anymore, but the collector is never-the-less caught in the legislation that should not pertain to these rare and beautiful machines, but has been lumped in there anyway.

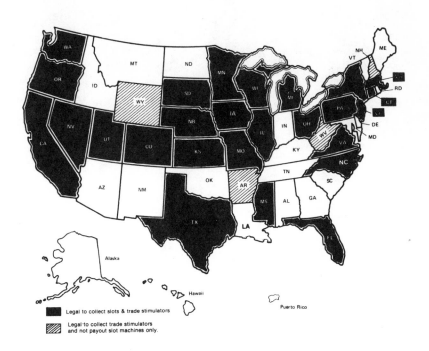

Legal to collect slots & trade stimulators

Legal to collect trade stimulators and not payout slot machines only.

I am not an attorney and do not pretend to understand all of these laws. I am not qualified to give legal advice, nor should anything in this book, text, or photos be construed to be anything but what is it, namely, information, specifications, and photographs obtained by the authors from various sources and believed, by the authors, to be reasonably accurate.

To get the legal information you need on your state laws and the legal status of your machines, the only advice I can give you is to see a local attorney.

 # Auction Fever

Many collectors and investors of antique slot machines can be frequently found at various slot machine auctions from New York to California. These auctions are held all throughout the year. An auction may be a good place to see and purchase antique slot machines if one knows machines. At auctions you buy "as is." You really must know if the case and mechanism is in good condition and good working order. Never bid on a machine you have not looked at. Some problems are: are all the parts there? are the parts and case original? what has been replaced? what does not work? Also, people tend to get carried away at auctions and sometimes pay more money for a machine than they would from a dealer or a collector.

Look at the various photos from a typical Pace Auction held in 1980. — Good Luck!

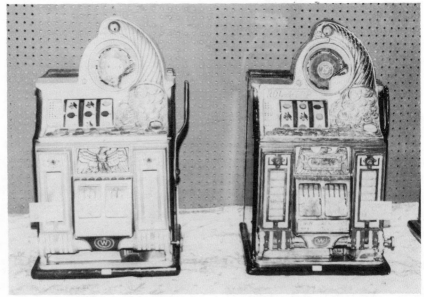

Slot Machines for Fun

Coin-operated amusement includes every type of machine which (a) is activated primarily by a coin and (b) is patronized by the public as a mode of the non-productive but psychologically beneficial human activity known as play.

Coin-operated amusement, therefore, includes not only the popular pinball games and such arcade equipment as target-shooting games, but also the coin-operated game of chance commonly called the slot machine. The slot machine is essentially a cabinet housing three or more narrow cylindrical drums, commonly called reels, which are marked with symbols. Vertically disposed on a common axis, the reels are caused to revolve freely, when player activates machine and pulls a lever-like handle affixed in the side of the cabinet. Awards, which are paid automatically, are based on the horizontal alignment of symbols, when the spinning reels come to a position of inertial rest.

For, although slot machine players desire to win, their basic motive is to experience the pleasure of anticipation and the intensified pleasure of fulfillment by periodic wins, large or small.

Indeed, the history of modern coin-operated amusement begins with the invention of the slot machine in 1895 by Charles Fey of San Francisco, California. Coin operated games of chance, based on dice or roulette, were used in the United States ten years prior to Fey's slot machine. However, the early machines never attained the popularity of the slot machine.

Nearly a century after the appearance of the early Fey slot machine, two persistent myths continue to prejudice appraisal of the machine as a form of amusement: first, that the percentage of intake which may be won by players is readily adjustable, up or down, by the owners of machines, merely by turning a concealed screw; second, that slot machines are engineered to favor the owners of machines, as against the players.

Commenting on the first myth, John Scrane, author of *Scarne's Complete Guide to Gambling* and a candid critic of sharp gambling practices, states that instant adjustability of slot-machines "is simply not true; the mechanism of a slot machine is quite complicated, and the payback odds cannot be changed unless the reel symbols are repositioned and the payoff slots adjusted to coincide with the changed combinations on the reels."

The second slot machine myth derives from the fact that early machines paid fifty percent of income to players, while some slot machine owners tampered with their equipment to prevent occurrence of the highest paying alignment of reel symbols.

However, modern slot machines are designed to be practically 100 percent tamper-proof, either by owners or players. And, as unauthorized operation of slot machines declined to the

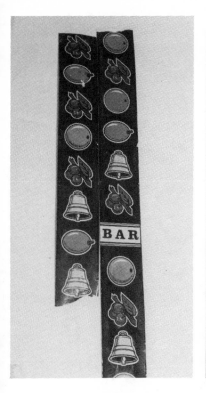

present status in which machines are largely confined to licensing jurisdictions—and owned by prudent businessmen, catering to a sophisticated clientele—the payout percentages have steadily risen.

Today very few slot machines are designed to pay out less than 78 percent of income. The average payout in leading licensed gaming areas is in the range of 85 percent, and numerous slot machines pay as high as 95 percent to the aggregate players. Each individual player is not assured of winning back 95 percent of the coins he deposits in a 95 percent machine. He may win more—as when, after playing a dozen coins, he walks away with a 200-coin jackpot—or he may win less. However, the total amount won by all the players patronizing the same machine, during a period of time, will be approximately 95 percent of the total amount deposited by players during the period. As one successful casino owner declares, "You've got to send out winners to get players."

Obviously, if a slot machine player resolves to play 100 coins in a machine designed to return to players 90 percent of coins

received, he may eventually play the entire 100 coins without his original fund being replenished from the machine. For 90 percent of 100 coins is 90 coins, 90 percent of 90 coins is 81 coins; and, as the player's available stake is diminished, the return in awards would diminish. However, sustained by periodic wins, large or small, a player would normally play during a considerable period of time before exhausting his original fund of 100 coins.

Slot machine critics assert that the player has "lost" 100 coins. With less violence to language in the context of a free

exchange, one may say that the player "spent" 100 coins for amusement. And in his predicament of having parted with the fund he resolved to play he is on equal terms with a person who resolves to spend a sum of money to hear a musical recital or witness a boxing contest: At the end of either performance, the patron is not refunded the price of admission. He knows that the impresario must pay rent and wages and realize a return on his investment. So must the impresario of slot machine amusement.

Certainly, money expended for the purpose of slot machine amusement is not lost to the economy of a community or nation. Coins deposited in slot machines pass from one owner to another, as in all exchanges. And an axiom of economics is that no type of exchange which fails to yield mutual satisfaction can permanently endure.

Substantial as the earnings of slot machines are—and they are massive, for example $180,510,866 in the state of Nevada during the fiscal year of 1969-1970—one may be sure that the portion which is not immediately returned to the economy of a community or nation in wages and taxes is quite promptly returned to the economy in purchases and investments. A major portion of slot machine profits may, indeed, enter into the capital formation which is the lifeblood of economic growth in every community and in all nations.

Slot Machines for Profit

Charles Fey was content to build only enough of his priceless invention, the slot machine, to supply his personal enterprise—rental of machines to San Francisco establishments on a share-profit basis. The Fey slot machine, therefore, was never exploited beyond the state of California.

However, a similar machine, produced in 1907 by Herbert S. Mills of Chicago, Illinois was vigorously promoted nationally and internationally.

Tradition tells that, when Mills sought a means to market his machine—a novelty unrelated to existing articles of commerce—he enlisted the cooperation of bankers, perhaps reasoning that bankers are trained to handle cash with care. He shipped his early slot machines on consignment to bankers in towns of medium size in every section of the United States. His only instruction was to place the machines in establishments frequented by the public, for he was confident that people would be attracted to a simple, convenient, low-priced form of amusement. He requested that a portion of the earnings be remitted to him until a stipulated price was paid. Thereafter, the machines were the property of the bankers.

The quick success of the slot machine suggests, first, that bankers were prompt to heed Mills' advice and, second, that they faithfully paid for machines delivered in trust—and, evidently, continued to buy machines. By 1910 slot machines, many built by competitors which Mills rapidly acquired, were in operation in most major cities of the United States, as well as in countless smaller towns, villages, and rural areas. Owners and players of slot machines, as well as all who scrutinized the colorful, ingenious devices, probably recognized the slot machine as a game of chance, subject to anti-gambling statutes. But in the early decades of the twentieth century the slot machine was often considered a trivial toy beneath the notice of the guardians of public safety.

Although bankers were probably the earliest professional owners of slot machines, they were soon joined by aggressive competitors who, observing the action which surrounded a slot machine located in a bar, billiard parlor, restaurant, or hotel lobby, shrewdly perceived the financial opportunity offered by the new amusement device, hastened to Chicago—center of a booming slot machine industry—to acquire all the slot machines their capital or credit might manage.

A vast new class of energetic entrepreneurs suddenly appeared on the stage of commercial life—slot machine operators. The term "operator" designates a businessman who buys coin-operated equipment and, while retaining title, installs the equipment in various establishments on a share-the-profit basis mutually agreeable to him and the proprietors of the establishments, which are called "locations."

The functions of an operator are to exercise experienced judgment in the selection of equipment, to maintain equipment in presentable and good working condition, and to circulate equipment among the locations he serves to insure continuous novelty. They were destined to play a role in the later popularization of other types of coin-operated amusement.

Although Mills adopted the Fey principles of (a) three revolving, symbol-bedecked reels, (b) the manually operated handle to spin the reels, and (c) automatic payment of awards in coins, he introduced two significant improvements in slot machine design.

Each reel on the first Fey machines bore only ten symbols. Thus, the possible combinations of symbols in horizontal alignment across the win-line was limited to 1,000 (10 × 10 × 10). Mills vastly increased the number by printing 20 symbols on each reel, producing 8,000 possible combinations (20 × 20 × 20). The 20-symbol, 20-stop system is in general use today.

The obvious advantage of a greater number of possible combinations of symbols on the win-line is that, by extending the mathematics of probability to the widest feasible range, (a) an enriched array of wins may be advertised on a slot machine to attract and hold the attention of players, (b) the frequency of wins may be considerably accelerated, and (c) the value of wins, particularly jackpots, may be notably increased.

Mills further improved the old Fey design by enlarging the window in the front of the cabinet through which the reels are viewed. Only three symbols in horizontal alignment were visible in the first Fey machines. Mills permitted players to see, not only the horizontal row of symbols across a central win-line, but also the rows directly above and below the center line, a total of nine symbols being constantly visible in the window.

The original purpose of the expanded symbol visibility was

to allow players to visualize the rich win potential. A non-winning alignment of symbols on the central win-line might often be bracketed between winning alignments above and below the central win-line, teasing players to continued play. In the course of time, the visibility of triple rows of symbols prompted development of interesting departures from the basic style of a single central win-line.

The Jackpot

The first outstanding advance in slot machine design, after the Mills contributions already described, was the jackpot with which Mills—hastily followed by his competitors—embellished his machines in 1925. The term "jackpot" is derived from the card game Draw Poker, in which the jackpot is the pool into which players enter their bets.

The original jackpot, now referred to as the drop jackpot, as distinguished from the guaranteed jackpots of today, was a metal container attached to a slot machine, the front of the container being transparent to display the coins contained.

The owner of a jackpot slot machine partially loaded the container with coins, then set the coin-handling mechanism of the machine to divert into the jackpot a percentage of all coins played into the machine. Thus, the jackpot was gradually filled to capacity.

The traditional jackpot alignment of symbols was three bars, which also paid 20 coins. Various other symbols are now favored as jackpot symbols, but the bar continues in the jackpot class. When three bars appeared on the win-line at the end of a spin, the jackpot container automatically opened, dropping the contents into the payout-cup.

Although the drop jackpot tremendously stimulated play, while the container sparkled with coins, the device was capable of stopping play on a machine. Players tended to avoid any machine which had recently delivered the jackpot.

A superstition of players is that, after a big win, a slot machine "slows down" and yields only small wins for a period of time. An empty jackpot container or a container showing only a dribble of coins was vivid evidence that the largest possible win had recently been paid. And players who did not subscribe to the slow-down theory recognized that three bars would yield only 20 coins, plus the few coins, if any, in the jackpot container. The boycott of an obviously "hit" machine usually continued until the manager of the establishment could call the owner of the machine to refill the jackpot.

The problem of the empty jackpot container was solved by the addition to slot machines of a second jackpot container, either on the face of the machine or concealed within the machines.

However, when the state of Nevada, in 1931, legalized all modes of gambling other than lottery, state regulations prohibited the variable and indeterminable jackpots delivered by the drop jackpot device. A jackpot in the state of Nevada—as in other jurisdictions around the world which license slot machines—must be of a specific value. The value of each jackpot must be conspicuously advertised on machines, and the advertised values must be guaranteed, i.e., must be paid in full, when won. Jackpot values may be expressed in the number of coins involved or in the currency value of the coins—or in tokens or replay credits.

New Problems Arise

Although introducing a businesslike certainty to jackpot technique, the guaranteed jackpot resulted in problems which plagued licensed slot machine owners for many years.

The coin-tubes from which slot machines, prior to 1963, paid wins lacked capacity to deliver the increasingly big jackpots which technical ingenuity developed. When a player won a jackpot of 50, 100, or 200 coins, he was obliged to call an attendant, who, after verification of the jackpot, gave the player a ticket, certifying the amount won and redeemable in cash by a central cashier.

Aside from the lack of showmanship inherent in attendant-paid jackpots, as compared to the sight and sound of a cascade of coins, the ticket method of paying jackpots led to abuses estimated to cost slot machine operators huge sums of money. The problem was not solved until the invention in 1963 of the Bottomless Payout Reserve.

 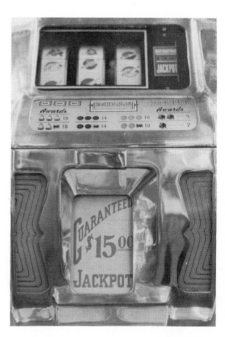

The Bottomless Payout Reserve

The first truly new slot machine since 1895 was introduced in 1963 and immediately won world wide fame and popularity among operators and players.

The new machine, the Bally Slot Machine, originated and manufactured by Bally Manufacturing Corporation, Chicago, Illinois, established in 1931 and now the world's largest producer of all types of coin operated amusements, not only preserves the slot machine characteristics, but also retains features of design which research indicates are indispensable to slot machine success.

(A) The power which causes the reels to spin is 100 percent mechanical, essentially the mechanical impact of spring-loaded reel-impellers, commonly called kickers, the springs being tensioned, then quickly and forcibly released, through a train of ratchets and gears activated by the player's forward and downward pull on a manually operated handle. Some Bally slot machines are not equipped with a handle and are activated simply by deposit of a coin. Reel action of such machines, however, is entirely mechanical, a motor merely supplying the spring-loading energy normally supplied by a player pulling a handle.

(B) The presence of ratchets is apparent to players through the "ratchet feel" familiar to players since the earliest days of slot machines.

(C) The free, uncontrolled spin and random, positive stop of the reels are entirely mechanical.

(D) General dimensions and styling—often called "slot look" styling—immediately identify the machine as a slot machine. Although as obviously a slot machine in appearance as the historic earlier machines, the Bally slot machine is styled with extravagant elegance new to coin operated amusement and artfully illuminated for maximum eye-appeal.

Beyond observance of slot machine traditions, the Bally slot machine is revolutionary in concepts, design, engineering, and construction, particularly in the use of electricity for invaluable purposes which do not alter the essentially mechanical action.

The introduction of electrical energy into slot machine technology resulted in advantages which slot machine operators were quick to recognize. Electricity was not entirely new to coin operated gaming equipment in 1963. As early as 1937, slot machine manufacturers introduced a type of electrically operated machine called a "console," probably from a dictionary definition of the word: "a cabinet (as for a radio or television set) designed to rest directly on the floor."

Although consoles continue in limited use, the machines do not rank with the typical slot machine in popularity.

(A) Reels and the various display signs of the Bally slot machines are illuminated, enhancing not only the eye-appeal of the machine, but also the visibility of win schedules and other directions to players; and concealed lamps cast a warm, wealthy glow on the deep, wide payout-bowl which in the Bally slot machine

replaces the small payout-cup of earlier machines.

(B) Illumination is extremely useful as a means to "personalize" a slot machine by display of the name, trademark, slogan, or other identification of a casino or club. Bally artists have produced several hundred individualized slot machine display signs, ranging from simply a distinctive name-style to an elaborate picture in colors of an entire hotel.

(C) The use of electrical circuitry to detect instantaneously the alignment of symbols at the end of a spin and, when a winning alignment occurs, to "telegraph" the appropriate award to the payout mechanism, insures precision, reliability, and speed never attained by the non-electrical mechanisms, which were subject to wear and maladjustment.

(D) Of greater importance, perhaps, than dependability is the fact that electrical circuitry in slot machines permits the development of an endless variety of new and fascinating win-systems, some of which are illustrated on other pages.

Jackpots Paid Automatically

Surmounting all other advantages of introducing electrical energy into the equation of slot machine design is the fact that the payout mechanism may be motor-operated, and, thus, vastly enlarged in coin-capacity.

The pay mechanism of the Bally slot machine includes a container with a capacity of 3,000 U.S. dime coins, which may be delivered in awards at a rate in excess of six coins per second. The container is often called "the Bottomless Payout Reserve" for the reason that the supply of coins available for payouts is never exhausted in normal play. Indeed, jackpots up to 200 coins are paid automatically in coins, significantly reducing the problems of jackpot payments previously described.

Jackpots in excess of 200 coins are necessarily attendant-paid to avoid excessive depletion of coins in the payout reserve; and all jackpots in machines operated with the U.S. half dollar and dollar—and coins of similar size—are usually paid by attendant. But the standard Bally slot machines pay all jackpots automatically in the most popular machines, i.e., machines played with U.S. five cents, dime, and quarter dollar—as well as coins of similar size in other nations.

The operator of the Bally slot machines, when placing a machine in operation, loads the payout reserve to capacity. Thereafter, an ingenious sensor device constantly "feels" the level of coins in the payout reserve. When, through continued payouts, coins in the reserve fall below a predetermined level, all coins played into the machine are automatically fed into the reserve. When the reserve again attains the desired level, coins played go directly to the coin-box from which the operator takes his income.

Although the level-sensing is mechanical—the sensor floating across the coins in the reserve—the signals to direct the flow of coins to the reserve or the coin-box are through electrical circuitry, again illustrating impact of electricity on slot machine technology.

Slot Machines Today

The endless variety of slot machines permitted by the use of electrical circuitry cannot possibly be described in detail in a general survey of coin operated amusement. The vast panoply of available slot machines may be suggested only by a brief summary of current major models.

(A) The standard slot machine uses three reels and is played with only one coin per pull of the handle with wins based on the alignment of symbols across a central win-line.

The standard slot machine is built in numerous different styles.

(B) A multiple-coin slot machine can be played with a single coin. Or a player may deposit several coins before pulling the handle, every win being multiplied by the number of coins played. The obvious advantage of a muliple-coin machine is that hourly income per square foot of floor space is notably increased.

(C) A special class of multiple-coin machine is the multiple-line machine. A typical multiple-line machine is the Bally 5-Liner, which permits a player to play one to five coins, at his discretion, to qualify one to five lines (three horizontal, two diagonal) as win lines. Wins are not multiplied by coins played, but a player can win on any lines played. One pull of the handle can produce wins on more than one line. An inducement to multiple coin play is the fact that the fifth line qualified by fifth coin, is the big jackpot line, often called the giant jackpot line.

(D) Another special class of multiple-coin slot machines is Bally Continental and other models in the Continental series, all of which are four-reel machines, offering players the option to play one to six coins, all wins being multiplied by the number of coins played, and an exceptionally brilliant array of wins.

(E) A Progressive slot machine is a machine in which the top jackpot, called the Super Jackpot, continuously increases in a predetermined ratio to coins played into the machine, the play being feverishly stimulated, as the Super Jackpot steadily climbs to an incredible peak of $9,999.

Super Jackpots are displayed on two separate Super Jackpot counters, which advance alternately, while red arrows light alternately to indicate the Super Jackpot which may be won at each moment of play. Thus, when one counter is reduced to the minimum figure by a Super Jackpot win, the other counter remains an inducement to continued play.

Progressive slot machines are available in single win-line models and multiple-line models.

(F) "Hold and Draw" refers to a popular style of slot machine which offers a player a "second chance" to win.

After a non-win spin, a hold signal is lit. A player may then press hold buttons to hold any desired reel or reels in a locked position, deposit a second coin and spin reel or reels not held to try again for a win. For example, if an orange appears on the first and third reels and another symbol on the middle reel, a player may hold the oranges and spin the middle reel in hopes of "drawing" another orange to fill out a triple orange win.

The state of the art in the slot machine industry is never static. New styles are continuously developed by imaginative designers.

Slot Machine Awards Used Today

Automatic payment of awards is a basic characteristic of the slot machine. But the media in which awards are automatically paid may vary considerably. Indeed, the manner in which the three major media, currency, tokens, and replay credits, are used and regulations pertaining to such use vary widely throughout the world. A summary of the three media and variants must necessarily suffice.

(A) Like the original slot machine, the most popular and presently most widely used machines automatically deliver awards in coins directly to players, or by the imperative of symbol alignment oblige the owner of a machine or his agent to pay large awards in currency.

(B) One type of token-pay slot machine may be activated either by coins or by the distinctive tokens with which the machines automatically pay awards; but awards are paid only in tokens. Coins played into a token-pay machine never enter the payout mechanism.

(C) A second type of token-pay machine may be activated only by tokens, which players purchase from the location management, and, of course, all payouts are in tokens.

(D) One type of replay-credit slot machine may be activated either by coins or by pressing a credit button to play off the replay credits in which awards are paid and which are registered on a visible credit counter.

(E) Another type of replay slot machine is activated only by a credit button. A player who desires to play buys a stated number of credits from the location attendant, who then registers the purchased credits on a visible credit counter by means of a key. All awards are in replay credits.

(F) An interesting type of slot machine combines certain advantages of replay credits with the special satisfaction of currency pay. Although wins are ultimately paid in currency, either automatically or in the case of large wins by attendant, all wins are first registered on a visible credit counter. A player in a mood for fast action can play off replays as rapidly as he can press the credit button and pull the handle. However, he can collect accumulated credits in currency whenever he desires by pressing a collect button.

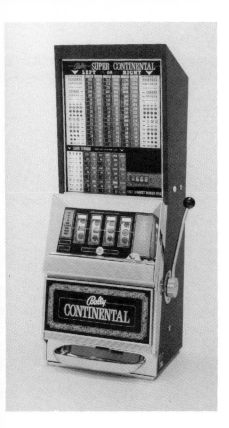

(G) Another type of machine is readily convertible by the
owner to either (a) currency pay or (b) replay credit
operation. The machine is thus adaptable to use
within one jurisdiction, to currency pay operation in

clubs and casinos or to replay operation in establishments frequented by the general public. Convertibility also facilitates resale from a jurisdiction, for example, which permits only replay operation into a jurisdiction which licenses currency pay machines.

The broad range of award systems available in modern slot machine technology is a primary reason for the increasing world wide use of slot machine as a popular and profitable form of coin operated amusements.

Mathematics of Slot Machines

Slot machine performance is regarded as darkly mysterious in the folklore of the general public, including numerous players, as well as critics who profess to be extremely knowledgeable on the subject of gaming equipment. However, the performance of a slot machine is based on relatively simple mathematics.

The schedule is the actual "paperwork" by which engineers of Bally Manufacturing Corporation designed a specific machine to return to the aggregate players 86.3 percent of coins played into the machine.

The upper section of the schedule states the quantity of the various symbols on each of the three reels, producing the 8,000 possible combinations on which the payout percentage is based. As related to awards, expressed in coins in the lower section of the schedule, the factor of 8,000 is also regarded as signifying 8,000 coins, the mathematical probability being that, during a period in which 8,000 coins are played into the machine portrayed by the schedule the machine will pay out 6,908 coins.

Under the title superimposed in the pay-schedule are data which illustrate an interesting technique by which the quantity of symbols on a reel are increased above the traditional twenty, thus increasing the variety of winning alignments.

The Seven over Bell arrangement consists of the numeral 7 printed over a bell with a sufficient portion of the bell visible to permit immediate recognition of the familiar bell symbol. Seven over bell in conjunction with other symbols in horizontal alignment on the win-line acts as either a 7 or a bell. Thus, if 7 over bell appears on one reel with bells on the remaining two reels, the machine "reads" the horizontal alignment as three bells and pays 18 coins. However, if 7 over bell appears across the win-line on all three reels, a triple 7 jackpot is paid, the super-imposed seven being the only seven symbols on the reels.

The use of superimposed symbols does not alter the basic

72

8,000 combinations previously described. Although symbols are pictorially added to reels, the number of stops (positions at which each reel can stop) remains limited to twenty.

Attention is directed to numbers enclosed in parentheses in the section of the pay-schedule which analyzes awards, e.g., (20-5) opposite "1 cherry" and under second reel. The notation is a shorthand expression signifying the following two factors: (1) the twenty stops of the second reel must be considered in calculating the number of possible combinations which include a cherry on the first reel; (2) all five cherry symbols on the second reel are allocated to double cherry wins, for, if a cherry on the first reel is followed by a cherry on the second reel, the alignment produces a double cherry win. Similarly, the notation (20-3) opposite "2 cherries" and under third reel indicates that, although the twenty stops of third reel cannot be ignored in calculation, all three cherry symbols on the third reel are involved in triple cherry wins.

Presentation of detailed pay-schedules for the multitude of different types of slot machines available would require a volume of considerable magnitude. The pay-schedule on page fifteen should suffice to suggest that slot machine performance, far from being an occult phenomenon, is as mathematically organized as a musical symphony. But in both the symphony and the slot machine the basic mathematical structure is gracefully concealed to enhance the pleasure of patrons.

Star Special   86.3% payout

	1ST REEL		2ND REEL		3RD REEL		
Cherry	3	×	5	×	3		
Orange	6	×	1	×	10		
Plum	7	×	1	×	4		
Bell	1	×	10	×	1		
Star	1	×	1	×	1		
Bar	2	×	2	×	1		
	20	×	20	×	20	=	8000

SUPERIMPOSED

Seven over Bell	1	×	2	×	1	
Eleven over Plum	2	×	1	×	1	
Target over Orange	1	×	1	×	2	

	AWARD AMOUNT								
1 Cherry	2	×	3	× (20 − 5) ×	20	=	1800	
2 Cherries	6	×	3	×	5	× (20 − 3)	=	1530
3 Cherries	10	×	3	×	5	×	3	=	450
3 Oranges	10	×	6	×	1	×	10	=	600
2 Oranges, Bar	10	×	6	×	1	×	1	=	60
3 Plums	14	×	7	×	1	×	4	=	392
2 Plums, Bar	14	×	7	×	1	×	1	=	98
3 Bells	18	×	1	×	10	×	1	=	180
2 Bells, Bar	18	×	1	×	10	×	1	=	180
3 Stars, **Showing in Any Position**	18	×	3	×	3	×	3	=	468
(Minus Center Line Position)								5758

PAYOUTS 5758
2242

JACKPOTS

3 Sevens	100	×	1	×	2	×	1	=	200
3 Elevens	100	×	2	×	1	×	1	=	200
3 Targets	100	×	1	×	1	×	2	=	200
3 Bars	100	×	2	×	2	×	1	=	400
3 Stars (**On Center Line**)	150	×	1	×	1	×	1	=	150
									1150

JACKPOTS 1150
NET INCOME 1092

SUMMARY

Total Play		8000	100.0%
Payouts	5758		72.0%
Jackpots	1150		14.3%
		6908	86.3%

TOTAL NET INCOME 13.7%

74

Social and Economic Benefits of the Slot Machine

From the earliest years of the slot machine, the spinning reels paid out generous contributions to charitable and civic endeavors. Volunteer fire departments, for example, in numerous towns and villages of the United States often depended significantly on two or three slot machines, owned and operated by the firemen, to generate funds for the purchase of fire-fighting equipment. Slot machines were formerly common in clubrooms maintained by associations of military veterans, ethnic groups, fraternal, and social organizations. Slot machines largely vanished from private clubs in the United States with the rise of the neo-puritanical spirit which presently appears to be diminishing in intensity. The machines in private clubs served a threefold purpose: (1) to provide relaxation and amusement for members and guests, (2) to subsidize maintenance of clubrooms, (3) to produce revenue for the favored charity which nearly every social society adopts. Indeed, an elderly pastor, reminiscing about the bygone era in which his left hand was not expected to be acutely aware of the pragmatic good works of his right hand, might recall borrowing slot machines from a local operator or neighborly slot machine manufacturer to enliven the church bazaar or carnival, and to raise money, not only for the church, but also for church-supported charity.

Slot Machines and the Economy

As the technological advance commonly called automation decreases the need for vast corps of labor in the extractive, productive, and distributive industries, the services industries—among which are the operation and maintenance of slot machines—assume a position of increasing importance to the economy of nations, an importance enhanced by the gradual enlargement of leisure time and disposable income. Within the service industries, the slot machine has already demonstrated ability to contribute to economic growth in specific areas of the world.

The small desert town of Las Vegas, Nevada, rapidly grew to a city with a population of 270,000, including environs, when hotels with casinos and specialized casinos were erected to compete with the earlier, and still thriving, resort and gaming center of Reno, Nevada.

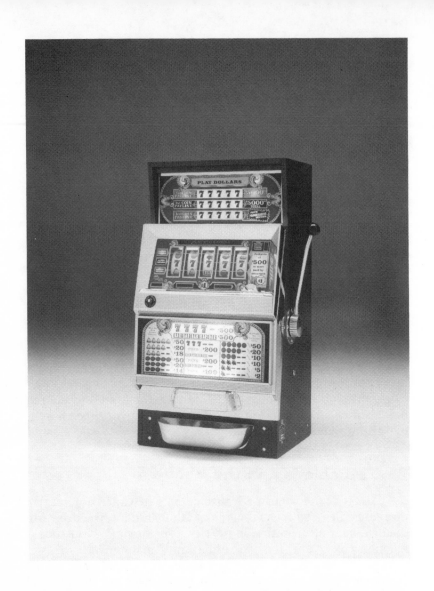

Similarly, when the Commonwealth of the Bahamas determined aggressively to promote tourism as a major national industry, an early official action was to authorize builders of resort hotels to include gaming casinos, with slot machines, in their plans. The example of the Bahamas was quickly followed in the Netherlands Antilles and other Carribbean island resort areas. Economic indicators clearly suggest that the introduction of slot machines has notably stimulated Carribbean tourism and, thus, economic growth. One more example of this is the new Las

Vegas East which is being built in Atlantic City, New Jersey; a once dying town is now coming back to life.

Economic growth in an area opened to slot machines is not limited to expansion of population in terms of mechanics and attendants in the service of slot machines and other employees of hotels and casinos. Personnel directly associated with the resort and gaming aspects of an area require food, shelter, and clothing. They require entertainment and recreation, schools, religious institutions, municipal services, banks, barber shops, beauty parlors, and all the establishments of a community. Such establishments rapidly enter the area or, if already in existence, expand. Like the wave caused by a pebble cast in a pond, economic growth initiated by pleasure resort enterprises, including the slot machine, spreads in an ever widening circle.

Slot Machine Benevolence

A slot machine operation was established to support charitable and other civic purposes, the Slot Machine Association in Finland.

The sphere of activity of the Association includes:
1. Promotion of general public health;
2. Support of child welfare;
3. Care of the blind, deaf, and dumb;
4. Support of the welfare of the disabled;
5. Support of the welfare of the aged;
6. Development of youth education;
7. Preparation for the protection and rescue of human lives in major emergencies; or
8. Procurement or maintenance of holiday sites open to all or promotion of comparable holiday facilities.

The list of social areas in which the Association is involved is quoted from a booklet published by the Association.

As the slot machine is increasingly accepted by society as a legitimate form of coin operated amusement, the slot machine may be expected to contribute increasingly to charitable and public welfare purposes. Although such contribution may in some nations involve governmental operation of slot machines or,

as in Finland, operation by quasi-public associations, the benefi-
cence of the slot machine in most jurisdictions of the world will
probably be effected through public taxation of privately owned
slot machines.

Our thanks to Mr. Herb Jones and Bally Manufacturing
Corporation for their help with this article.

No book on slot machines would be complete without some
comment and photographs of Mayor Fiorello LaGuardia, New
York City's world famous mayor. Mayor LaGuardia loved publicity, whether it was reading the Sunday comics to the children
over the radio because of a newspaper strike, marching in
parades, or his most famous of photographs, splashed across
front pages of American newspapers—swinging that sledge
hammer and breaking those slot machines. I wonder what he
would say today, not only of their beauty and value, but of all the
State games, Numbers, Lotto, Slot, Pick Three, and hundreds
more as various states scramble for the taxpayers' dollar.

LaGuardia smashing slot machines 10/13/34.

LaGuardia hits the Jack-Pot.
A one man wrecking crew with sledge hammer as he works on a mountain of
slot machines and other gambling devices confiscated by the police department.
Scene on a police barge as the contraband machines were towed out to Long
Island Sound, destroyed, and dumped.

The following prices are for a current range of slot machines in good to mint-mint condition. Keep in mind this is a retail price range and is believed to reflect fair, up-to-date prices at this time. Prices were compiled by the authors from various sources thought to be reasonably accurate.

3. Rare and Early Slot Machines

Caille 5¢ "Centaur" "Big Six" Double One-Wheel Slot Machine In An Upright Case, circa 1910. The oak cabinet carved and beaded and with scroll and floral cast metal mounts, each machine complete with a color-coded six-way coin head and a central glass revealing the gambling color wheel. Restored condition. H. 63". **$20,000–35,000**

Very rare Mille "Roulette" 5¢ Payout Gambling Machine, in hexagonal standing oak case with carved work and marquetry, supported on six cast iron claw feet, and with other cast iron fittings. When handle is cranked steel ball spins around the moving roulette wheel before landing in one of the eighty spaces, with seven different payout possibilities totalling 10¢ to $2.50. 1900. H. 41½".

$22,000–35,000

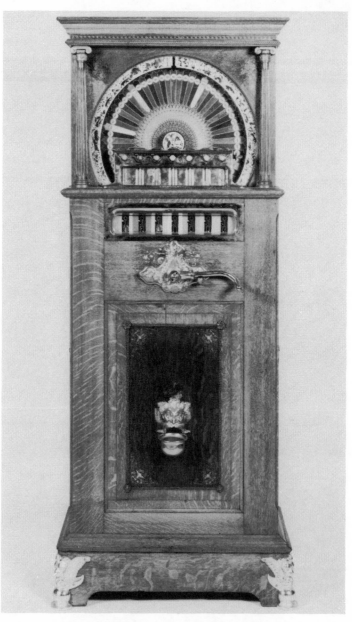

A Berger "Oom Paul" 5¢ Single Reel Mechanical Upright Slot Machine, in carved oak case, embellished with marquetry and cast iron fittings, the chromolithographed wheel flanked by two fluted columns, with seven possible betting combinations. Circa 1901, excellent restored. This machine, named after a hero of the Boer War, was one of the tallest uprights made and is rare in mechanical form. H. 73". **$10,000–18,000**

A Caille "Newcentury Puck" 5¢ Upright Single-Wheel Slot Machine, with green stained oak cabinet and copper plated cast iron trim with six coin slots. Circa 1901, excellent restored. H. 68". **$8,000–14,000**

Gabel's 5¢ "Chicago" One-Wheel Slot Machine In An Upright Case, contained in the original oak cabinet with cast metal mounts and gilt scroll decoration, the central glass revealing the gambling color wheel Circa 1910. "Original" condition. H 64". **$7,000–11,000**

Illinois Tool Co. "Star Detroit" 5¢ One-Wheel Slot Machine with Music Box, the upright oak case with beading complete with a color-coded six-way coin head, an inset glass panel below revealing the music box. Circa 1900. H. 64½".

$5,000–11,000

Mills "Dewey Jackpot" 25¢ Single-Wheel Upright Slot Machine, in oak case with copper-plated cast iron ornamentation and marquee, and reverse-painted circular glass front. The Dewey Jackpot enjoyed an unusually long production (1902-1926) due to its immense popularity. Circa 1915, excellent original condition. H. 70". **$7,000–10,000**

*Mills "Dewey" 5¢ One-Wheel Slot Machine in an Upright Musical Cabinet, the
oak cabinet carved and beaded with scroll cast metal mounts and inset with the
original reverse-painted-on-glass portrait of Admiral Dewey, the interior applied
with original labels including an inspection label dated 1902. Circa 1900.
H. 66".* **$8,000–11,000**

Mills 5¢ "On The Square" One-Wheel Upright Slot Machine, contained in the original oak cabinet with cast metal mounts, the central glass revealing the gambling color wheel. Circa 1900. H. 68".   **$5,500–8,000**

Rare Caille "Puritan" 5¢ One-Wheel Slot Machine in an Upright Case, one of the two known examples. The oak cabinet carved and beaded, inset with the original glass applied with a printed scene of cupids at play, the motif reflected below in a cast metal medallion, the interior with original label, complete with the shipping crate marked "Puritan." Circa 1900. H. 64". **$8,000–14,000**

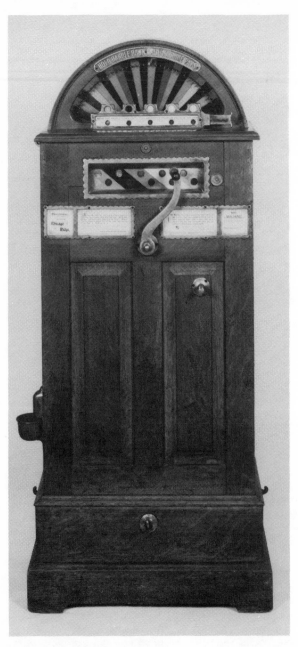

A Berger "Chicago Ridge" 5¢ Single-Wheel Upright Slot Machine, with electric payout mechanism, in oak case with arched top, with original award and instruction cards. Circa 1897, excellent original condition. H. 57".

$5,000–8,000

Watling 5¢ "Jefferson" One-Wheel Counter-Top Model Slot Machine, with a six-way coin head contained in an oak case. Circa 1910. H. 22". **$2,000–4,000**

Watling 5¢ "Exchange" One-Wheel Counter-Top Model Slot Machine, with a five-way coin head mounted on an oak case. Circa 1910. H. 20".

$2,000–3,500

Schall "Horseshoe and Eagle" One-Wheel 5¢ Slot Machine, the counter-top model with a single pinwheel mechanism within a wood case. Circa 1896. H. 21". **$2,000–3,500**

Berger Chicago Ridge 5¢ One-Wheel Battery-Operated Slot Machine In An Upright Case, the standing rectangular oak case with a semi-spherical top with glass inset revealing the color gambling wheel, with central handle, and side payout cup. Circa 1897. Restored. H. 56". **$5,000–8,000**

A "Pace's Races" 5¢ Horserace Gambling Machine, with seven horses racing along parallel tracks, electrically powered and pneumatically activated with changing odds and varying payout rates; contained in a streamlined wood console cabinet. The "Pace's Races" is considered to be the most sophisticated of the coin operated gambling machines. L. 50". 1934, excellent restored.

$2,500–7,500

Mills Slot Machines

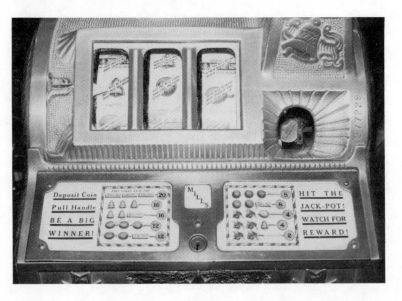

MILLS		Fortune Chicago	1903
Admiral	1899	50¢ Chicago	1903
Dewey	1899	Fortune Dewey	1905
Chicago	1900	Dewey Triple	1907
Check Dewey	1901	Operator Bell	1917
Dewey Jackpot	1902	Gum Vendor	1917
Dewey Twin	1902	Counter Vendor	1920
25¢ Dewey	1903	OK Vendor	1921
50¢ Dewey	1903	Club Console	1921

Front OK	1923	Future	1936
Owl	1924	Yellow War Eagle	1936
Bell	1925	Cherry Front	1937
Bell	1926	Horse Head	1937
Baseball	1927	Diamond	1937
Front OK	1928	Counter Club Bell	1937
Counter	1929	Golf Ball Vendor	1937
Front OK	1929	Counter Club	1938
Baseball Vendor	1929	Mystery Club Console	1938
New Yorker	1930	Black Front	1938
Gooseneck Bell	1931	Brown Front	1938
Gum Ball Vendor	1931	Country Club	1938
Lion's Head	1931	Cherry Vendor	1938
Modern Head	1931	Console Club Bell	1938
Silent FOK	1931	Chrome Vendor	1939
Silent Jackpot	1931	Chrome Front	1939
Gum Ball Vendor	1932	Club Double Bell Console	1939
Double Skyscraper	1932	High Topper	1939
War Eagle	1932	Bonus Bell	1939
Silent Vendor	1932	OK Mint Vendor	1939
Roman Head	1932	7-7-7 Bell	1939
World's Fair	1933	Black Beauty	1940
Extraordinare	1933	Gold Chrome	1941
Grey Vendor	1933	Copper Front	1941
Golden Bell	1933	Front Vendor	1942
Silent Mystery	1933	Free Play	1942
Blue Front	1933	Double Bell	1943
Golden Vendor	1933	Chrome War Eagle	1943
Grey Front	1933	Black Cherry	1945
Skyscraper-Goose	1933	Golden Falls	1946
Century	1934	Four Bells	1946
Silent Modern Front	1934	Jumbo	1947
Century Bell	1934	Bonus	1947
Futurity	1936	Jewel Bell	1947
Bursting Cherry	1936	Jackpot	1948
Orange Front Vendor	1936	Blue Bell	1948

Mills 5¢ "Operator's Bell" Three-Reel Slot Machine, with a cast iron case, this example one of the early three-reel designs. Circa 1911. H. 25". **$6500.**

Mills 5¢ "Operator's Bell" Cast Iron Front Three-Reel Slot Machine, with brass-plated cast iron and wood case. Circa 1915. H. 24". **$2,000–4,000**

Mills 5¢ "F.O.K." Three-Reel Slot Machine, with fortune reel strips and front mint vendor. Circa 1923, partially restored. **$1,500–2,500**

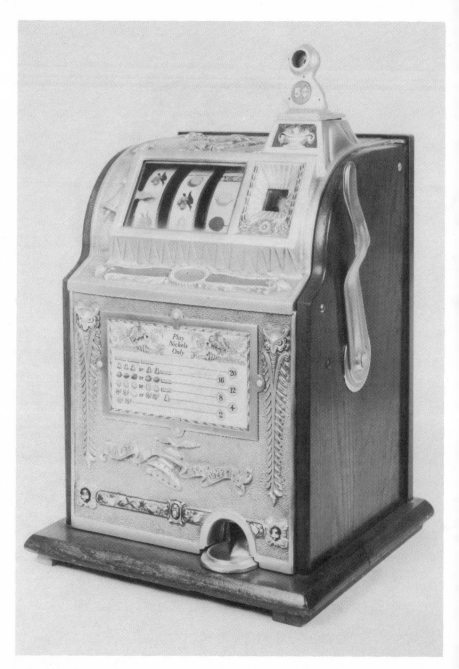

Mills 5¢ Gooseneck Three-Reel Slot Machine, dated on front casting. Circa 1923. H. 26". **$1,200–2,200**

Mills "Automatic Salesman" 5¢ Three-Reel Slot Machine, with side vendor and elaborate cast aluminum front, a central window indicating winnings or "mints." Circa 1923, good original condition. H. 24½". **$1,700–2,700**

1923 Mills Operators Bell. This was the first year they went from cast iron castings to aluminum castings and everyone else in the industry did the same right after. This machine is very similar to the Watling except Mills used an owl and Watling, I believe, used an eagle. Many were made with side vendors and were called a variety of names in the 20s, from OK Bell to C OK, Counter OK, and Silent Salesman. **Price not available**

Mills "Automatic Salesman" 5¢ Three-Reel Slot Machine, with a side vendor, the front case with bells and owl head. Circa 1923. H. 25". **$1,700–2,700**

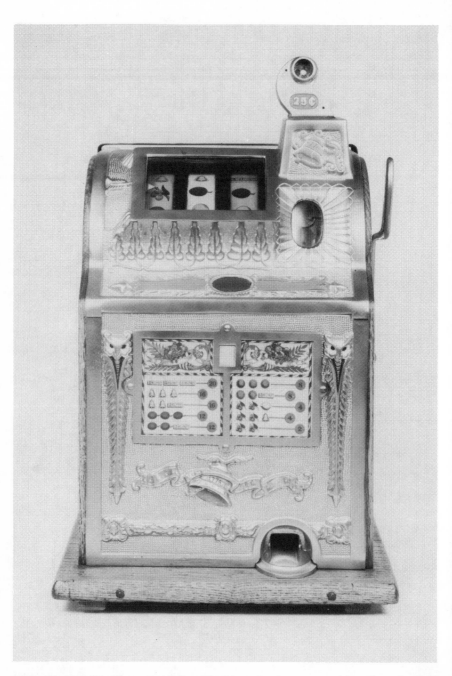

*Mills "O.K." 25¢ Three-Reel Slot Machine, the front cast with owls and a bell.
(1924.) H. 25½".* **$1,300–2,300**

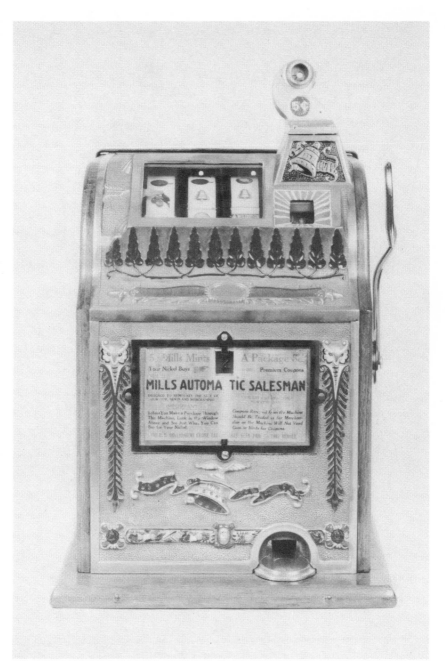

Mills 5¢ "Automatic Salesman" Three-Reel Slot Machine. Circa 1925. H. 26".
$1,200–2,200

Mills 5¢ "Liberty Bell" Three-Reel Slot Machine, with fortune reel strips. Circa 1928, partially restored. **$1,500–2,500**

Mills 25¢ "Poinsettia" Three-Reel Slot Machine, with a jackpot and skill stop buttons. Circa 1928. H. 25". **$1,400–2,400**

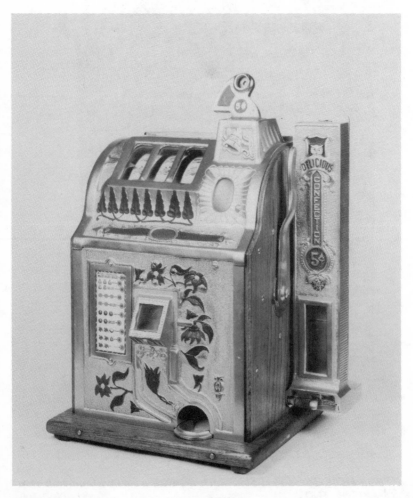

Mills "Poinsettia" 5¢ Three-Reel Slot Machine, with single jackpot side vendor and fortune reel strips. Circa 1928. H. approximately 26". **$1,600–2,600**

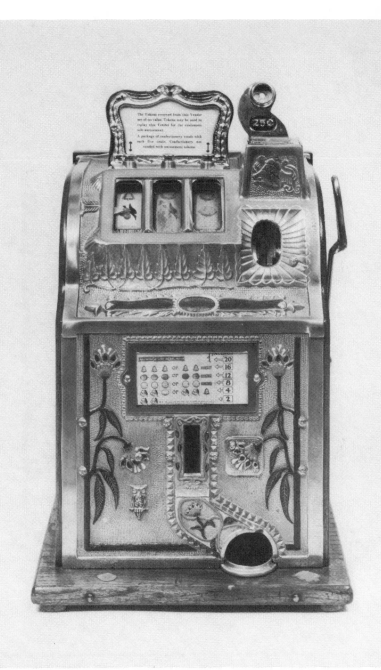

Mills 25¢ "Poinsettia" Three-Reel Slot Machine, with single jackpot and skill stop buttons. Circa 1928, partially restored. **$1,300–2,300**

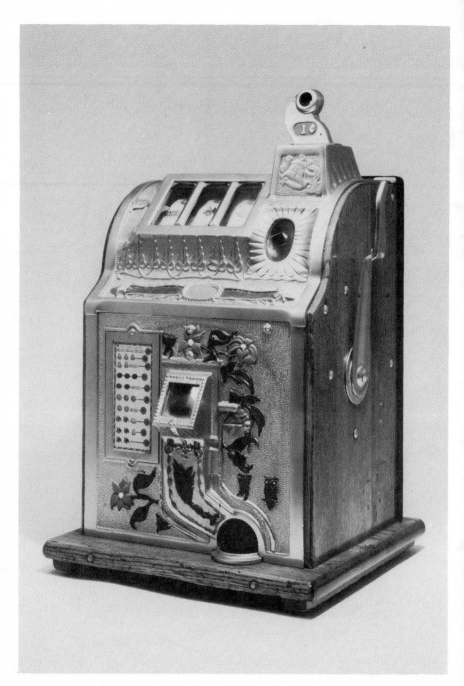

Mills 1¢ "Poinsettia" Three-Reel Slot Machine, with single jackpot. Circa 1928, partially restored. **$1,200–2,200**

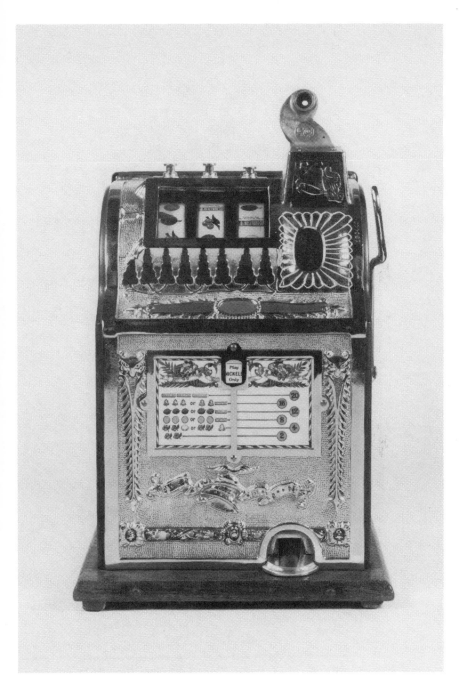

Mills "C.O.K." 5¢ Three-Reel Slot Machine, with skill stops to arrest the reels.
Circa 1924 H. 25½".   **$1,250–2,250**

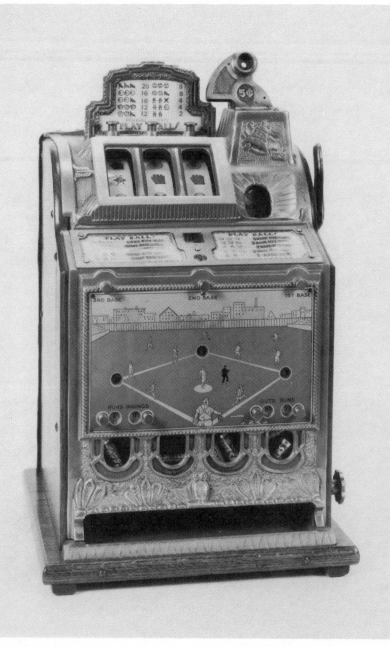

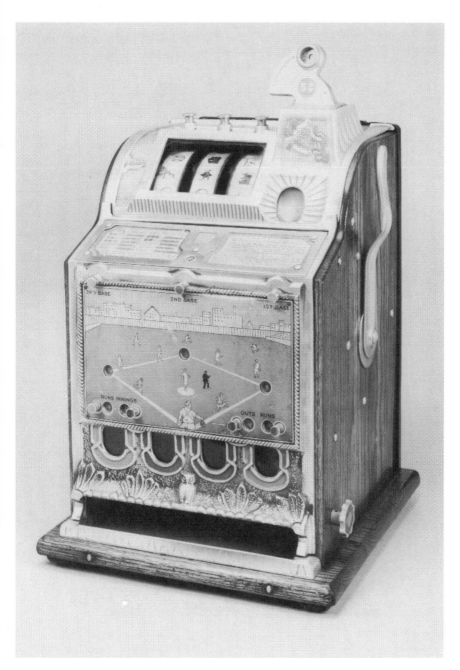

Mills "Baseball O.K. Vendor" 5¢ Three-Reel Slot Machine, equipped with skill stops to arrest the reels, printed with baseball symbols, with four chutes to dispense mints. Circa 1929. H. 27". **$3,000–4,000**

Mills 5¢ "Baseball" Three-Reel Slot Machine, with baseball reel strips and front mint vendor. Circa 1929, partially restored. **$3,150–4,150**

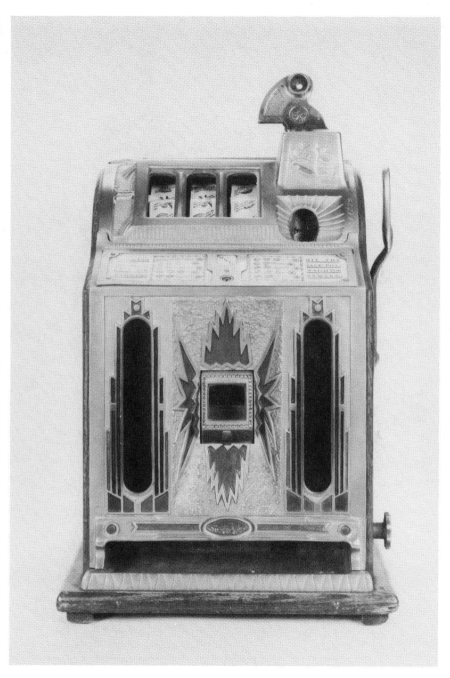

Mills "Jackpot" 5¢ Three-Reel Slot Machine, equipped for vending mints with a jackpot and fortune reel strips. Circa 1930. H. approximately 26". $1,500–2,500

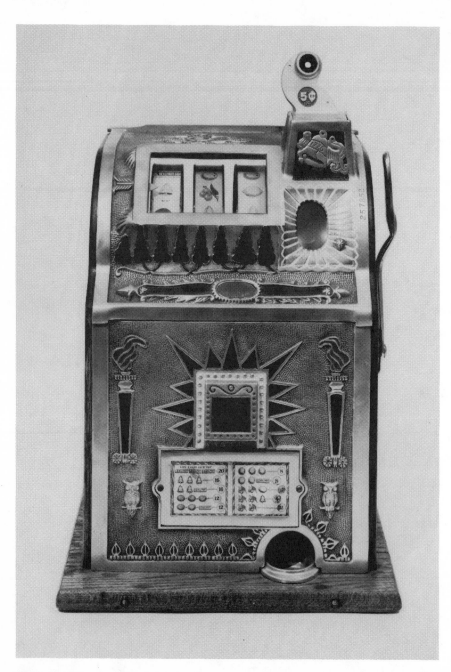

Mills 5¢ "Torch Front" Three-Reel Slot Machine, with single jackpot, Circa 1930, partically restored. **$1,300–2,300**

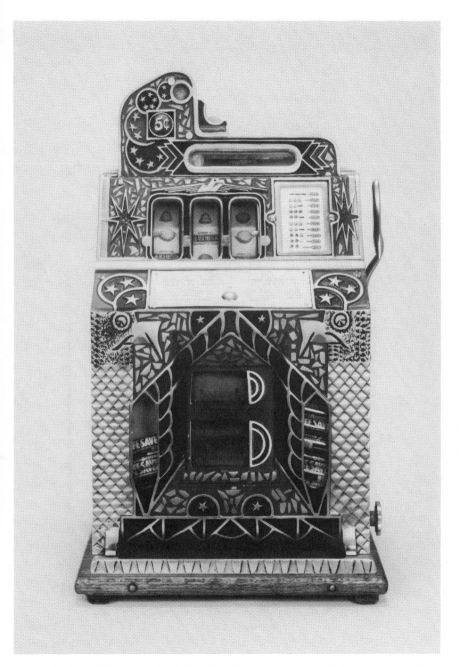

Mills "F.O.K." 5¢ Three-Reel Slot Machine, equipped with front mint vendors, with a double jackpot, detailed in green, red, and black. Circa 1931. H. 26".
$1,700–2,750

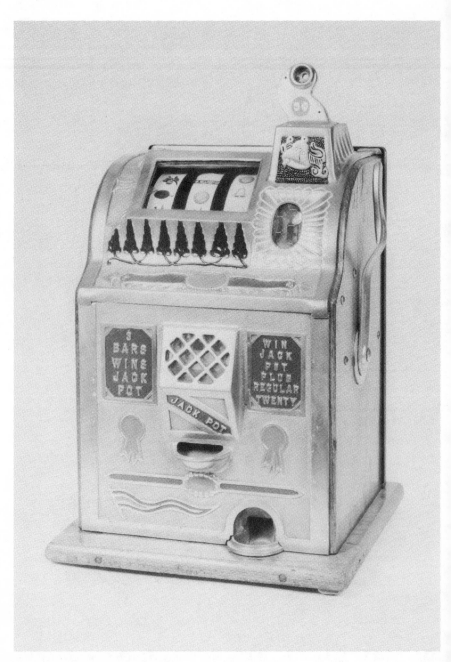

Mills 5¢ Gooseneck Three-Reel Slot Machine with Roberts Conversion Front, with a jackpot. Circa 1931. H. 26″. **$1,500–2,500**

Mills "Super Bell" 5¢ Lion Head Three-Reel Slot Machine, with a jackpot. Circa 1931. H. 25". **$1,800–2,800**

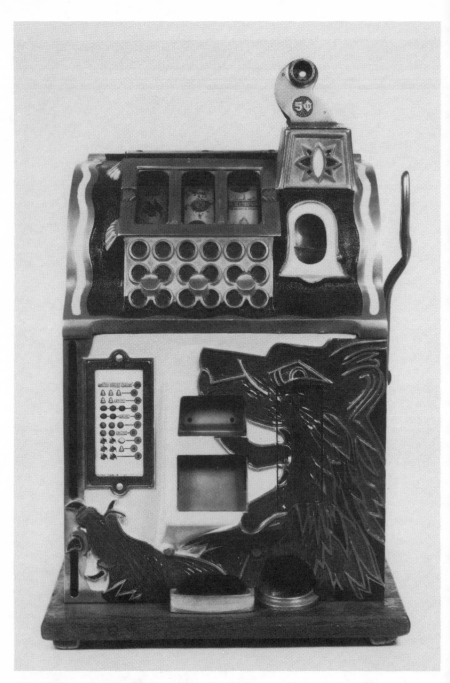

Mills 5¢ "Super Bell Lion" Three-Reel Slot Machine, with a double jackpot. Circa 1931. H. 26". **$1,800-2,800**

Mills 5¢ "Super Bell Lion" Three-Reel Slot Machine, with unusual single jackpot. Circa 1931, fair "original" condition. **$2,000–3,000**

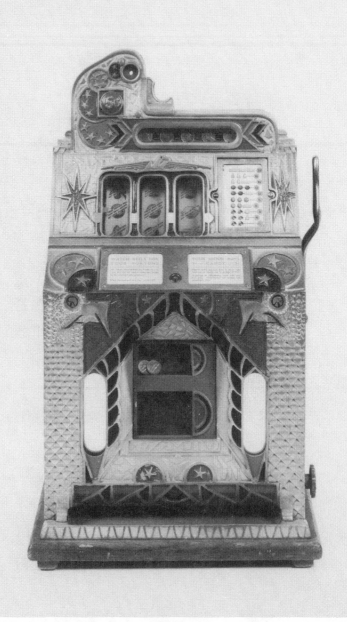

Mills "Silent F.O.K." Three-Reel Slot Machine, with fortune reel strips, twin jackpots, and front mint vendors. Together with 100 tokens. Circa 1931, fair "original" condition. H. approximately 28". **$1,800–2,850**

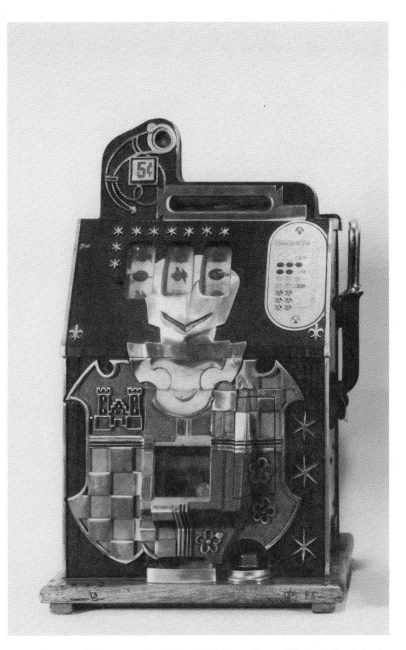

Mills "Castle" 5¢ Three-Reel Slot Machine. Circa 1934, good original condition.
H. 26½".   **$1,500–2,500**

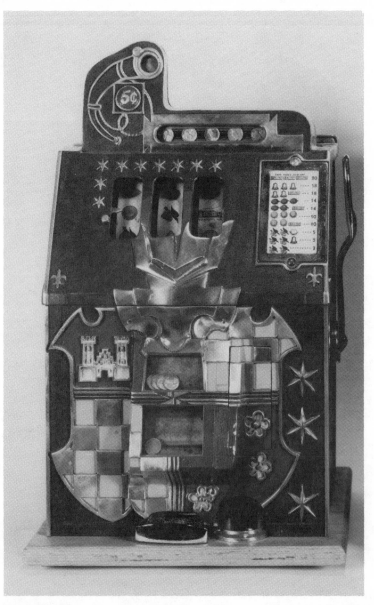

Mills "Castle" 5¢ Three-Reel Slot Machine. Circa 1933, good restored.
H. 25¾". **$1,400–2,400**

Mills "Futurity" 5¢ Three-Reel Slot Machine, with side vendor. This machine is equipped with a mechanism which returns all the player's nickels if he should lose ten times in a row. **$3,500–4,500**

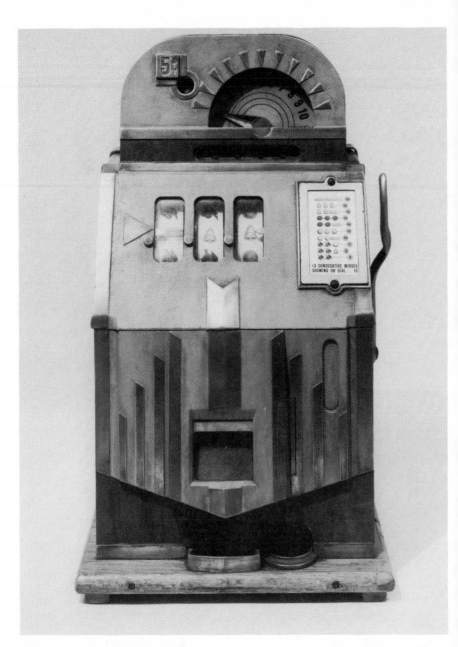

Mills 5¢ "Futurity" Three-Reel Slot Machine, the front cast in Art Deco taste with a single jackpot, surmounted by an indicator advancing with each loss to a total of ten, then specially awarding ten coins, but equipped with a cheating device to increase the probability of winning. Circa 1936, very good original condition including reel strips. **$3,050–4,050**

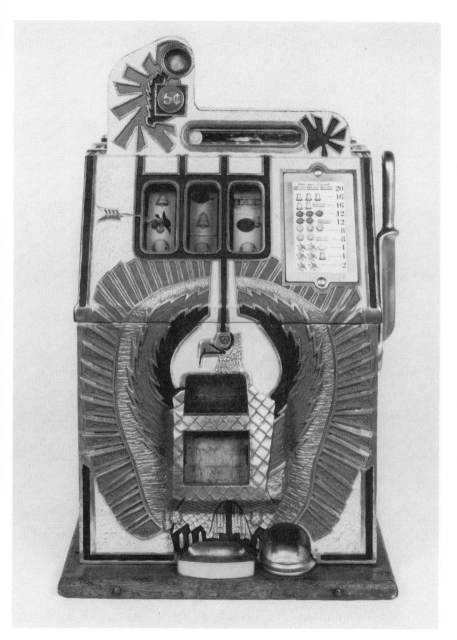

Mills "War Eagle" 5¢ Three-Reel Slot Machine, the front detailed in yellow, red, and black, with a jackpot. Circa 1931. H. 26". **$2,200–3,500**

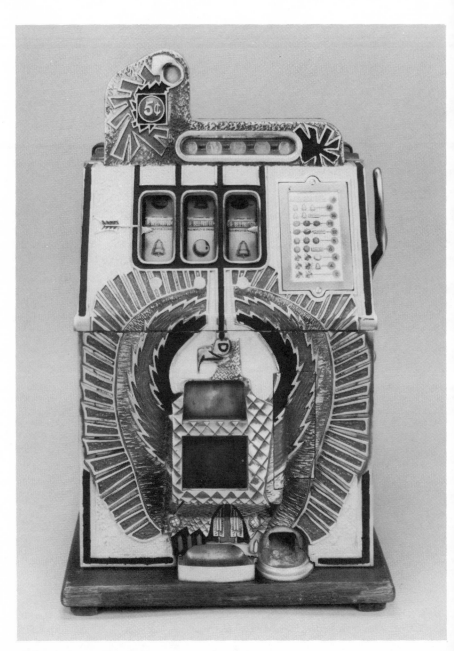

Mills "War Eagle" 5¢ Three-Reel Slot Machine, the front detailed in yellow, red, and black, with a jackpot. H. 26½".
$2,200–3,500

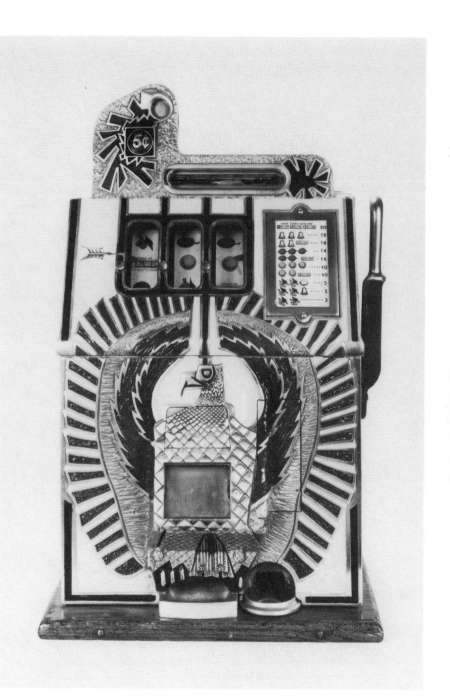

Mills "War Eagle" 5¢ Three-Reel Slot Machine, with a jackpot. Circa 1931. H. 26". **$2,300–3,600**

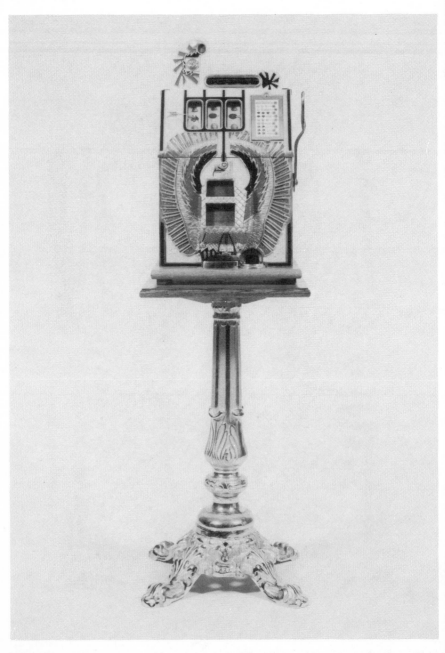

Mills 25¢ "War Eagle" Three-Reel Slot Machine, with twin jackpots. Circa 1931, partially restored. **Price not available**

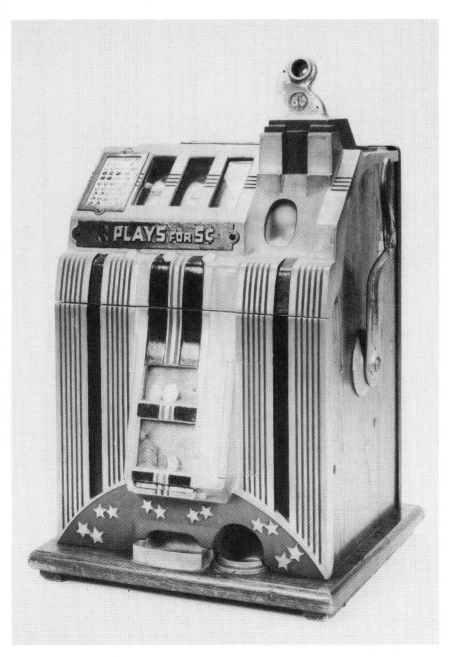

Mills "Skyscraper" 5¢ Three-Reel Slot Machine, with a double jackpot, the front cast with stripes and stars painted blue and black. Circa 1932. H. 26".

$1,400–2,400

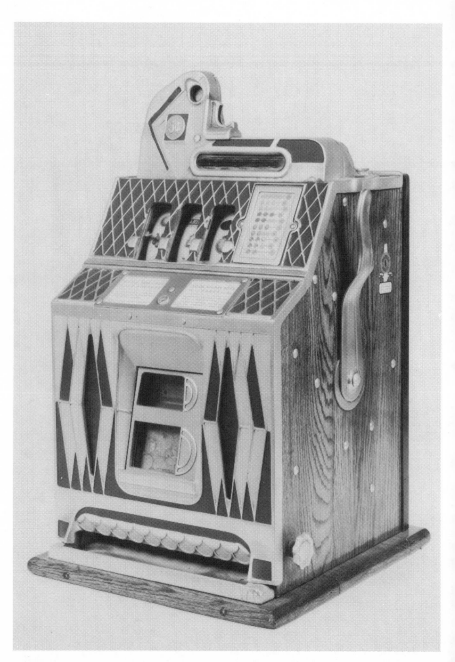

Mills 5¢ "Mystery Front" Three-Reel Slot Machine, with jackpot and equipped to vend mints. Circa 1932. H. 26". **$1,700–2,700**

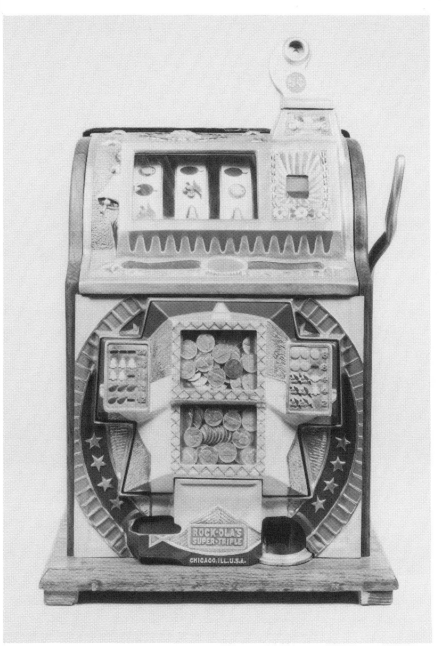

Mills/Rockola 5¢ "Triple Jackpot" Three-Reel Slot Machine. Circa 1932.
H. 26".   **$1,400–2,400**

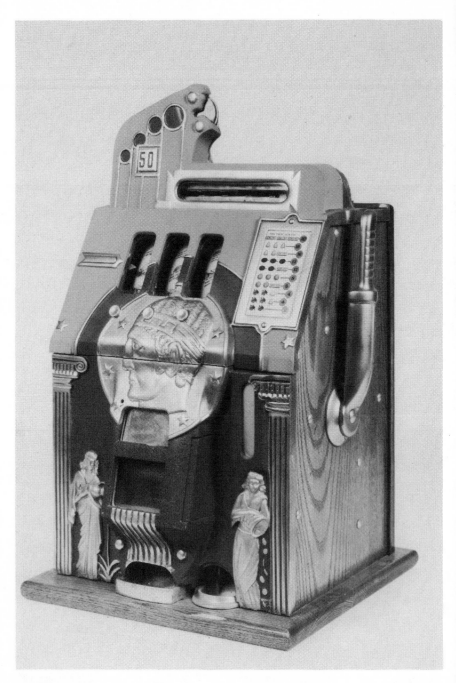

Mills 50¢ "Roman Head" Three-Reel Slot Machine, with a jackpot. Circa 1932.
H. 26".   **$1,800–2,700**

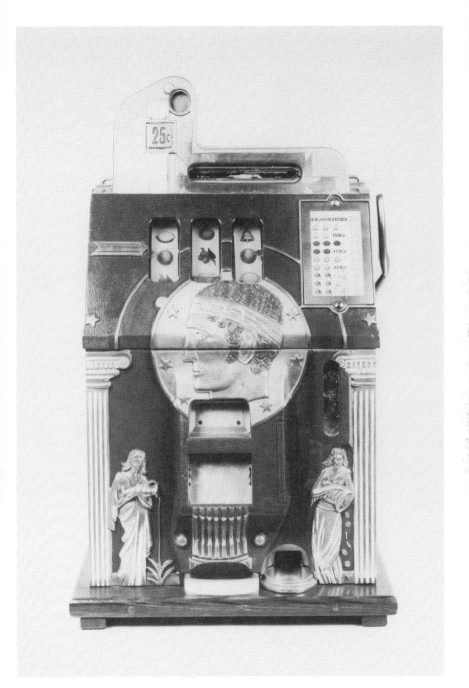

Mills 25¢ "Roman Head" Three-Reel Slot Machine, with a jackpot and a gold award feature. Circa 1932. H. 26". **$2,000–3,000**

Mills 5¢ "Roman Head" Three-Reel Slot Machine, with fortune reel strips and gold award token. Circa 1932, partially restored.   **$2,000–3,000**

Mills "Roman Head" 25¢ Three-Reel Slot Machine, in upright console case, the machine front modelled with a large gilt Roman coin. Mid-1930s, excellent restored. H. 58". **$2,750–3,750**

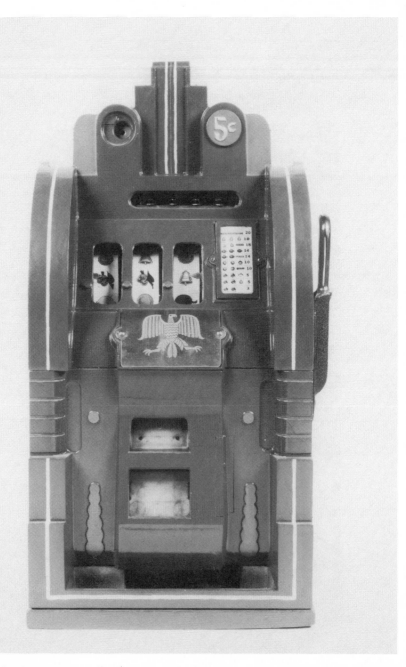

Mills 5¢ "Extraordinary" Three-Reel Slot Machine, with a double jackpot. Circa 1933. H. 29".   **$1,250–2,250**

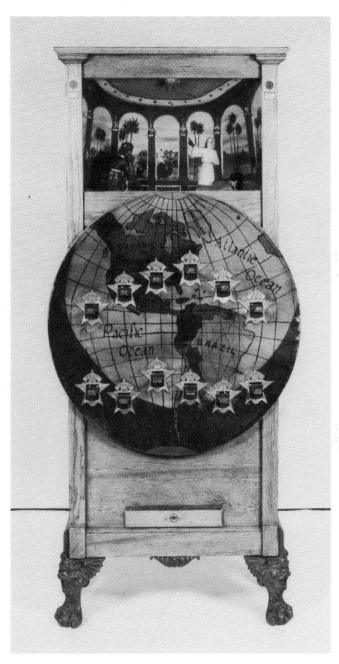

Mills "Horoscope" Fortune Telling Machine, the large wooden case with elaborate cast iron fittings, the handles modelled with the Mills owl logo. Circa 1920. 78 x 36 x 16½".   **$2,500–3,000**

Mills Four Column Front Vendor 5¢ E-Reel Slot Machine, with future pay mechanism, working mint vendors, original award card, and tin lithographed reel strips. This machine contains a future pay mechanism with no jackpot, working on the theory that if the player could see what he would win before inserting his coin, he wasn't gambling. Circa 1933, good original condition. H. 26½". **$2,000–3,500**

Mills "Pace Conversion" 5¢ Three-Reel Slot Machine, the cast aluminum front housing two columns for mints, with twin jackpots. Mint vendors were added to slot machines in order to evade anti-gambling laws. If a customer was "buying" mints with every play, he was not technically gambling. 1930s, restored.

$2,000–3,500

Mills 1¢ Three-Reel Slot Machine, equipped to vend gum, with a jackpot and fortune reel strips. Circa 1933. Height 26½". **$2,500–3,700**

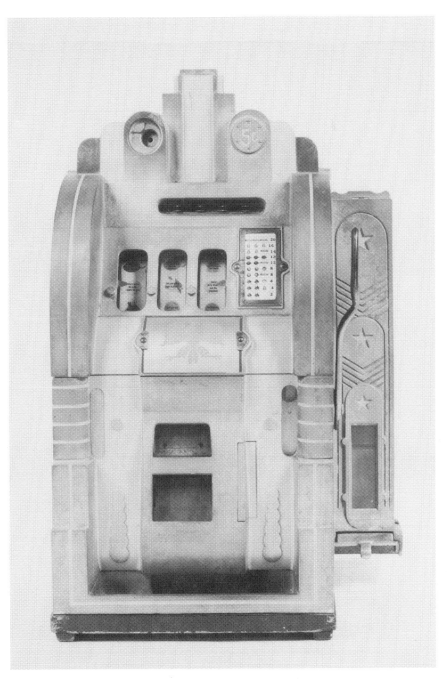

Mills 5¢ "Extraordinary" Three-Reel Slot Machine, with gold award token feature and side mint vendor. Circa 1933. H. 29" **$1,600–2,600**

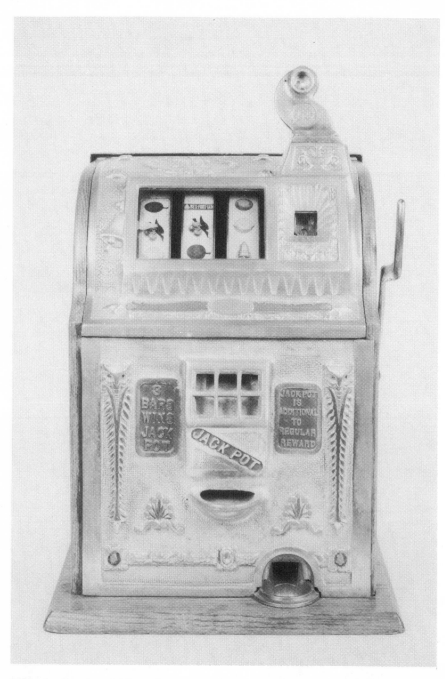

Mills 5¢ Gooseneck Three-Reel Slot Machine With Roberts Conversion Front, with a jackpot. Circa 1935. H. 26". **$1,300–2,300**

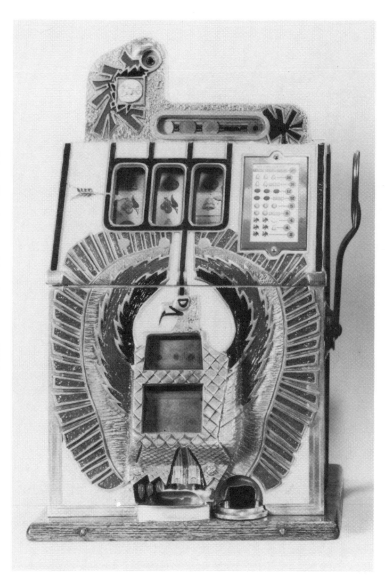

Mills "War Eagle" 25¢ Three-Reel Slot Machine, the front case cast with an Art Deco stylized eagle. Circa 1935, excellent restored. H. 25" **$2,250–3,500**

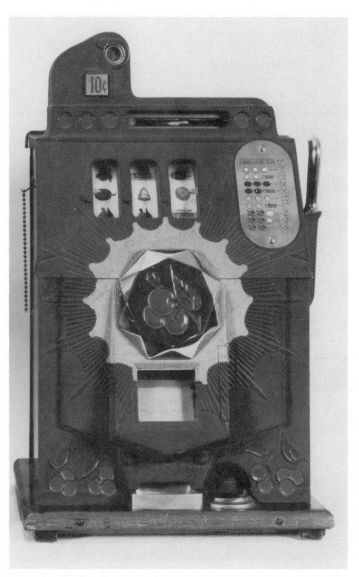

Mills "Bursting Cherry" 10¢ Three-Reel Slot Machine. The "Brown front" design was employed to make the machine less conspicuous. Circa 1938, excellent original condition. H. 25½". **$1,500–2,500**

Mills "Automatic Dice" 25¢ Gambling Machine, operates in the manner of a dice table game, on original stand. This machine was considered too complex by the average player and was therefore produced for only a short period of time. Circa 1934. H. 58".   **$3,000–4,000**

Mills 10¢ "Bursting Cherry" Three-Reel Slot Machine, with an oak turned pedestal stand. Circa 1936. H. 27". **$1,800–2,800**

Mills "Gooseneck" 5¢ Three-Reel Slot Machine, the front cast with a hunting scene. Circa 1935. H. 26". **$1,200–2,200**

Mills 5¢ Gooseneck Three-Reel Slot Machine with Roberts Conversion Front, the front cast with figures playing cards. Circa 1935. H. 26". **$1,300–2,300**

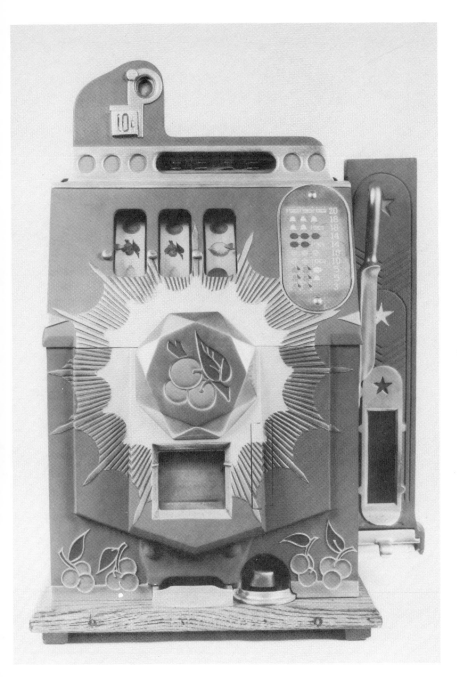

Mills 10¢ "Bursting Cherry" Three-Reel Slot Machine, equipped with a side gum vendor. Circa 1936. H. 26". **$1,900–2,950**

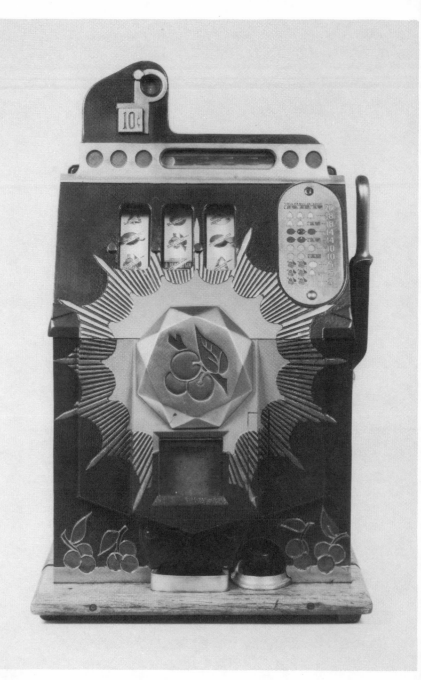

Mills "Bursting Cherry" 10¢ Three-Reel Slot Machine, with a jackpot and fortunes printed over the traditional reel symbols. Circa 1937. H. 26".

$1,600–2,600

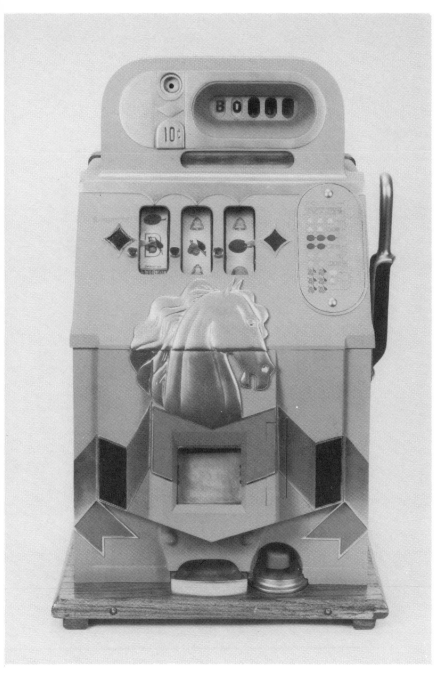

Mills "Horse Head Bonus" 10¢ Three-Reel Slot Machine, with a jackpot. Circa 1937. H. 26". **$1,600–2,600**

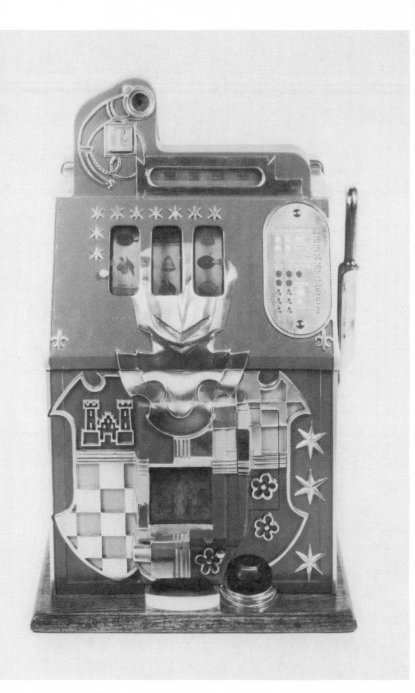

Mills "Castle Blue Front" 1¢ Three-Reel Slot Machine, the front detailed in blue and red, with a jackpot. Circa 1937. H. 26½". **$1,500–2,550**

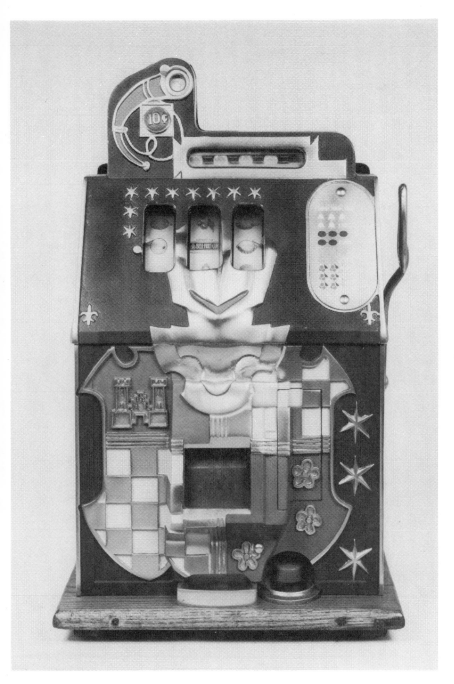

Mills "Castle Blue Front" 10¢ Three-Reel Slot Machine, with a jackpot. Circa 1937. H. 25". **$1,550–2,550**

Mills "Hi-Top" 1¢ Three-Reel Slot Machine, with jackpot. Circa 1939. H. 26".
$1,200–2,200

Caille "Centaur" — a colorful seven-coin head and matching glass color wheel set off this very ornate oak upright one-wheeler. Fancy jackpot castings and intricately carved oak cabinet. Circa 1908, H. 63".

$9,000-12,000

Watling "Jackpot" oak upright with six-coin head and colorful glass wheel with jackpot in reverse on glass, ornate casting around jackpot payout. Circa 1902, H. 64". **$10,000-14,000**

Caille "Twin Centaur" — "Play nickels, play quarters," is what it says on the marquee over twin coin heads on this rare carved oak and beaded upright. Scroll and floral castings with color-coded coin head and glass gambling color wheel. Circa 1909, H. 63". **$22,000-25,000**

"The Owl" — this is the upright that started it all. It was the first successful slot machine ever made. It introduced the five-way multiple coin head with matching color wheel. The owls on the glass later became the logo for the Mills Company. Mills Novelty Company, circa 1898, H. 67".

$4,500-6,500

Mills "20th Century" — what better way to celebrate the new century than with this new, large, highly carved oak upright. Its eight-way coin head was cast with its name flanked by two winged maidens on top of a reversed, silver painted glass color wheel. Circa 1900, H. 68". **$8,000-12,000**

Bally 5¢ "Reliance" $5.00 Jackpot dice payout gambling machine. Circa 1936, H. 18". **$3,500-6,000**

Mills "Check Boy" — an early 5¢ counter machine with a six-way head. The machine could also pay out trade checks, hence its name. Highly ornate case in nickel and brass. Circa 1908. **$4,500-7,500**

Watling "Exchange" — 5¢ oak counter model slot machine with five-way coin head and glass color wheel. Circa 1910, H. 20".   **$3,500-5,000**

Watling "Treasury" — a very colorful gooseneck with skill stops. Ornate top castings, including an eagle and cascading coins, flank the twin jackpot. Truly one of the most beautiful counter models ever made. Circa 1936, H. 25 ½". **$4,500-6,000**

"Spear the Dragon" amusement machine, oak case with cast aluminum upper portion painted with a dragon and twin figures of St. George. You tested your nerve by holding player knobs which gave a mild electric shock until bell rang. Exhibit Supply Mfg. Co., circa 1927, H. 73 ½". **$4,000-5,000**

Mills Cast Aluminum "Liberty Bell" — a fancy and rare machine, with all four sides having heavy castings. Circa 1929, H. 24". **$3,000-6,500**

Mills "Baseball Vendor" with baseball reel strips and probably the most interesting front of any slot machine. Along with its four column mint vendor and marquee, this front-played baseball machine is complete with players, a green playing field, and bleachers. It keeps a total of runs, innings, outs and whose on first, second, and third base. The Mills Owl can be found at the bottom front of the machine. Circa 1929, H. 27". **$3,000-4,000**

Caille "New Century Puck" — an elaborate oak upright with fancy glass color wheel and castings, six-way color coded coin head. Circa 1902, H. 65". **$11,000-14,000**

Watling "Roll-A-Top" — front casting with cascading coins spilling out of a horn which leads up to the coin slot. Bottom front casting with eagle flanked by coins and a glass double jackpot. A real beauty. Circa 1935, H. 27". **$3,200-4,700**

Mills "Hi-Top" 10¢ Three-Reel Slot Machine, jackpot payout, not from machine. Circa 1940. H. 26". **$1,200–2,200**

Mills "Hi-Top" Black Beauty Three-Reel Slot Machine, jackpot payout not from machine. Circa 1940. H. 26". **$1,250–2,250**

Jennings
Slot Machines

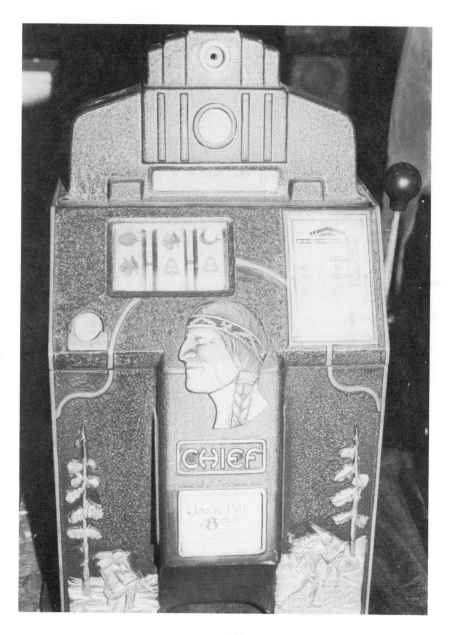

JENNINGS

Gooseneck	1920	Dixie Bell	1937
Operator's Bell	1920	Ciga-Rola Console	1937
Operator's Console	1920	Chief Console	1937
Automatic Counter	1920	Silver Chief	1937
Today Vendor	1926	Gold Ball Vendor	1937
Blue Boy	1926	Sky Chief	1938
Dutch Boy	1929	Triplex Chief	1938
Jackpot Bell	1929	Big Chief	1939
Victoria Witch	1930	Silver Moon Console	1940
Baseball	1930	Victory Chief	1941
Dutch Boy Jackpot	1930	Bronze Chief	1941
Victoria	1931	Silver Club	1941
Rock-A-Way	1931	Silver Moon	1941
Little Duke	1932	Airplane	1941
Peacock	1932	Silver Moon Chief	1941
Dutchess	1933	Club Chief	1945
Derby Special	1933	Black Hawk	1946
American Derby Horse Race	1933	Silver Eagle	1946
Century Bell	1933	Standard Chief	1946
Electro-Jax	1933	Deluxe Console	1947
Century	1933	Challenger Console	1947
Prosperity	1934	Lucky 7	1948
One Star Chief	1935	Tic-Tac-Toe	1948
Four Star Chief	1936		

Jennings Pace Conversion 1¢ Three-Reel Slot Machine, with a jackpot, the front detailed in blue, red, and yellow. This machine has an award card although it is not illustrated. Circa 1919. H. 26½". **$1,300–2,300**

Jennings 5¢ "Operator's Bell" Three-Reel Slot Machine, with fortune reels and wood sides. Circa 1920. H. 26". **$2,700–3,700**

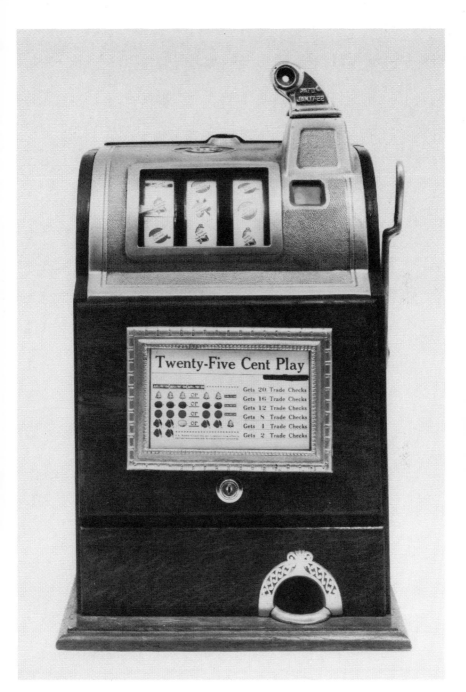

Jennings 5¢ "Operators Bell" Wood-Front Three-Reel Slot Machine, with fortune reel strips. Circa 1920, partially restored. **$2,700–3,700**

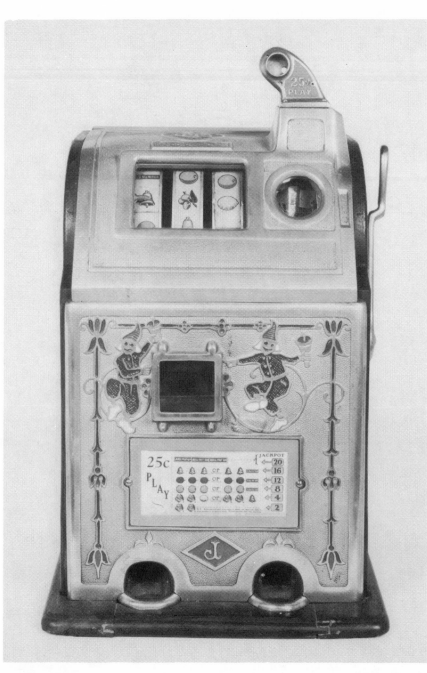

Jennings "Dutch Boy/Dutch Girl" 25¢ Three-Reel Slot Machine, with a jackpot. Circa 1929. H. 24½".   **$1,450–2,450**

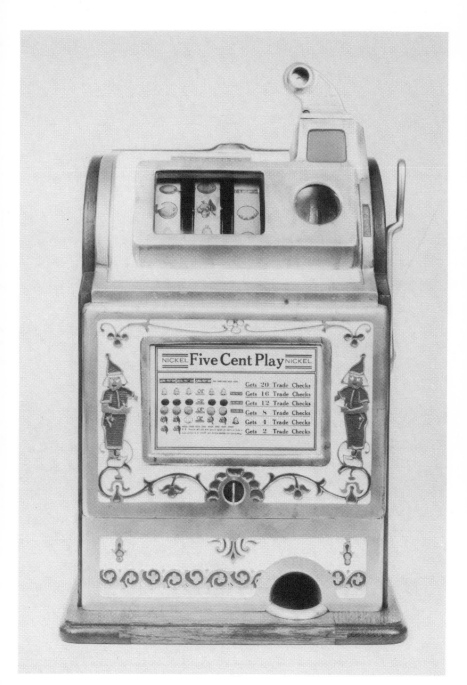

*Jennings 5¢ "Dutch Boy and Girl" Three-Reel Slot Machine. Circa 1929.
H. 26"* **$1,300–2,300**

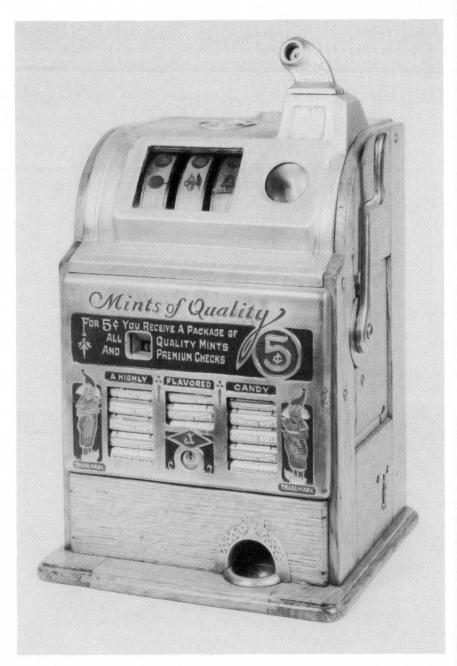

Jennings "Dutch Boy/Dutch Girl" 5¢ Three-Reel Slot Machine, with front mint vendor. Circa 1929. H. 25". **$1,600–2,600**

Jennings 5¢ "Today" Three-Reel Slot Machine with Front Vendor, with fortune reel strips. Circa 1926, partially restored. **$1,900–2,900**

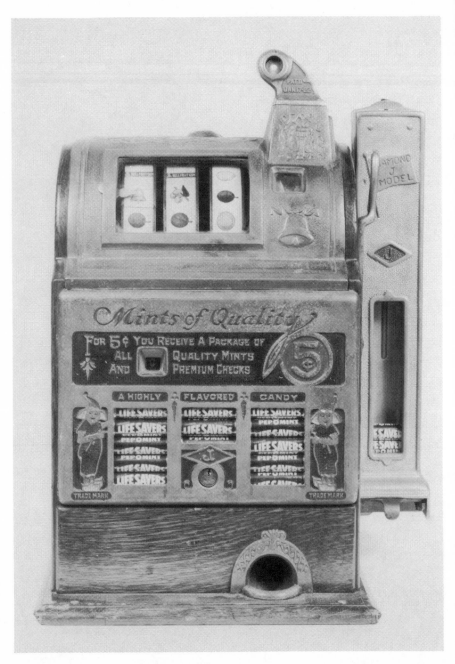

Jennings 5¢ "Dutch Boy and Girl" Three-Reel Slot Machine, equipped with both front and side mint vendors and a "future pay" mechanism indicating potential winnings. Circa 1929. H. 26". **$1,900–2,900**

Jennings "Peacock" Three-Reel Slot Machine, with twin jackpot and a front mint vendor. Circa 1932. H. 26". **$2,500–4,000**

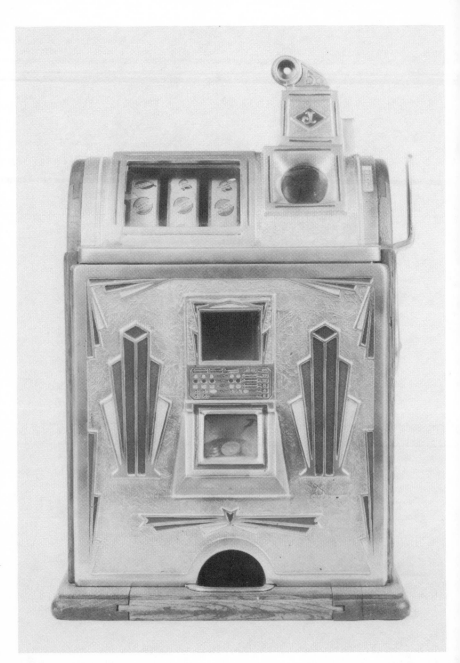

Jennings 5¢ "Victoria" Three-Reel Slot Machine, with two jackpots and fortune reel strips. Circa 1932. H. 25". **$1,500–2,500**

Jennings 5¢ "Victoria" Three-Reel Slot Machine, with a single jackpot. Circa 1932, fair "original" condition. **$1,400–2,400**

Jennings "Little Duke" 1¢ Three-Reel Slot Machine, cast in Art Deco taste and with a jackpot. Circa 1932. H. 25".   **$1,750–3,100**

Jennings "Little Duke" 1¢ Three-Reel Slot Machine, the Art Deco front painted yellow, red, green, blue, and black, with a jackpot. Circa 1932. H. 22½".
$1,800–3,200

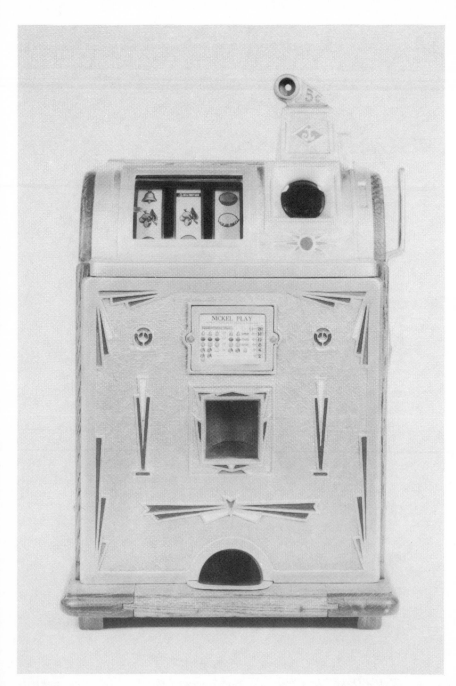

Jennings 5¢ "Victoria" Three-Reel Slot Machine, with a jackpot. Circa 1932.
H. 25".   **$1,400–2,400**

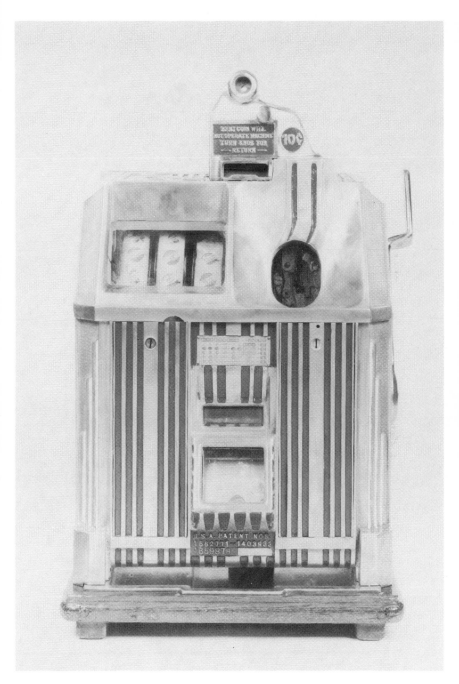

Jennings 10¢ "Duchess" Three-Reel Slot Machine, with fortune reel strips. Circa 1933. H. 24".　　　　　　　　　　　　　　　　　　　　　　**$1,100–1,900**

Jennings "Duchess" 5¢ Three-Reel Slot Machine, the front vendor with the mints or candy displayed behind windows flanking the jackpot, with the original decal. Circa 1934. H. 20". **$1,700–2,700**

Jennings "Duchess 5¢ Three-Reel Slot Machine, with mint vendors flanking a jackpot. Circa 1934. H. 22½". **$1,600–2,600**

Jennings 5¢ "Century Vendor" Three-Reel Slot Machine, with a double jackpot and fortune reels. Circa 1934. H. 27". **$1,600–2,600**

Jennings "Today" 5¢ Three-Reel Slot Machine, with four mint vending columns, the case cast with flowers and elfin figures, with rotating award cards and unusual reel strips. Early 1930s, good original condition. H. 26¼". **$1,900–2,900**

Jennings "Escalator Peacock" 5¢ Three-Reel Slot Machine, with Art Deco style cast aluminum case in an elaborate geometric design incorporating three peacocks. Circa 1934. H. 25½".   **$2,600–4,000**

Jennings 5¢ "Four Star Chief" Three Reel Slot Machine, with single jackpot. Circa 1936, partially restored. **$1,400–2,400**

Jennings 25¢ "Sky Chief" Three-Reel Slot Machine, with single jackpot. Circa 1938, restored. **$1,300–2,300**

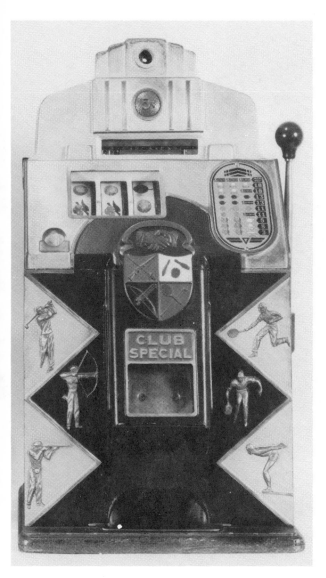

Jennings Sportsman "Club Special" 5¢ Three-Reel Slot Machine, the front cast with various athletic motifs and a sporting coat of arms. This rare model was made especially for country club use. Circa 1936, excellent original condition. H. 28". **$3,000–3,500**

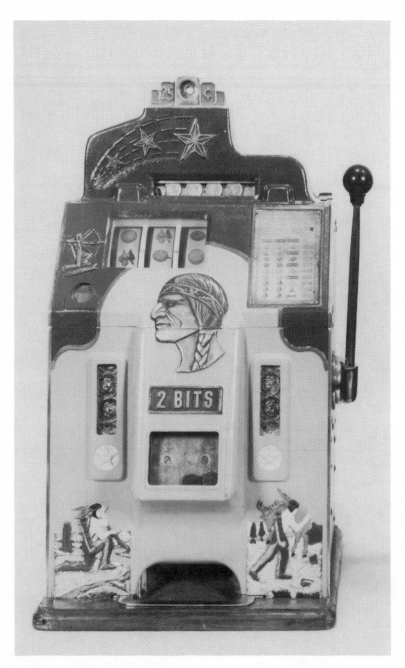

Jennings "Chief" 25¢ Three-Reel Slot Machine with double gold prosperity award, special "2 bits" cast front. 1930s, excellent restored with original award card and reel strips. H. 27". **$1,500–2,500**

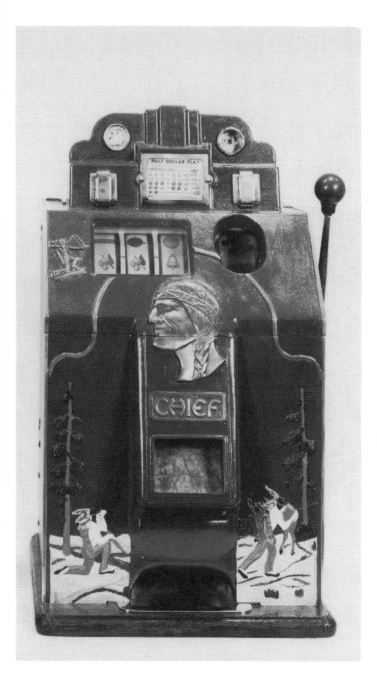

Jennings "Chief" 50¢ Three-Reel Slot Machine, the front cast with bronze Indian head and hunting scenes. The 50¢ denomination is rare for this machine. 1930s, excellent restored. H. 26". **$1,500–2,500**

Jennings Two-Column Mint Vendor 5¢ Three-Reel Slot Machine, with textured cast aluminum front inset with geometric motifs. Circa 1935, excellent condition. H. 26". **$1,700–2,700**

Jennings "Victoria" 5¢ Three-Reel Slot Machine, the front cast with Art Deco style skyscrapers on either side of the twin jackpot window. 1930s, excellent restored. H. 26".   **$1,500–2,500**

Jennings "Sportsman" 25¢ Three-Reel Slot Machine, the wood cased front fending mechanism dispensing golf balls. Circa 1937. H. 23". **$800–1,800**

Jennings 5¢ and 10¢ "Cigarola" Cigarette Vending/Slot Machine.   Circa 1937, good "original" condition.   **$600–1,600**

Watling
Slot Machines

WATLING

Venus Upright	1899	Twin Jackpot	1931
Brownie Counter	1900	Twin Jackpot Gum Vendor	1931
Marquette Upright	1901	Twin Jackpot Front Vendor	1931
Uncle Sam Upright	1901	Baby Gold Award	1932
Buffalo Upright	1901	Wonder Bell	1934
Chicago Upright	1902	Gold Award	1934
Cupid Upright	1902	Blue Seal	1934
Detroit Upright	1902	Ball Gum Vendor	1934
Dewey Upright	1902	Rol-A-Tor	1935
Fox Upright	1902	Rol-A-Tor Vendor	1935
Owl Upright	1902	Rol-A-Tor Ball Gum	1935
Lonestar Upright	1902	Rol-A-Tor Gold Award	1935
Judge Upright	1902	Rol-A-Tor Silent	1935
Duck Upright	1902	Rol-A-Tor OK	1935
Triple Upright	1902	Rol-A-Tor Gold Front	1935
Big Six Upright	1903	Rol-A-Top	1935
Forty Five Upright	1903	Rol-A-Top Vendor	1935
Jackpot Upright	1904	Rol-A-Top Ball Gum	1935
Golden Gate Counter	1908	Rol-A-Top Silent	1935
Operator's Bell	1910	Rol-A-Top OK	1935
Brownie Improved	1910	Rol-A-Top Gold Award	1935
Little Six Counter	1910	Rol-A-Top Gold Gum Ball	1935
Jefferson Counter	1910	Rol-A-Top Gold Front	1935
Billiken Counter	1911	Treasury Vendor	1936
Check Boy Counter	1911	Cherry Front	1936
Pastime Counter	1911	Cherry Bell	1937
Totem Counter	1911	Rol-A-Top Baseball	1937
Bungalow Counter	1913	Diamond Vendor	1937
Eagle	1918	Diamond Bell	1937
Jackpot Gum Vendor	1920	Rol-A-Top 25¢	1938
Excelsior Counter	1920	Melon Bell	1938
OK Jackpot	1920	Future Play	1938
Lincoln Delux	1926	Diamond Bell	1938
Blue Seal Front Vendor	1927	Rol-A-Top Front Load	1939
Brownie Jackpot	1929	Rol-A-Top Mint Vendor	1940
Blue Seal Jackpot	1929	Rol-A-Top Console	1940
		Rol-A-Top Extra Award	1947

A Watling "Exchange" 5¢ Single-Wheel Slot Machine, rare table model, with token payout. This machine is a combination of early cast iron token payout and the table-top cash payout machine. Circa 1930s, excellent restored. H. 19½".

$3,500–5,000

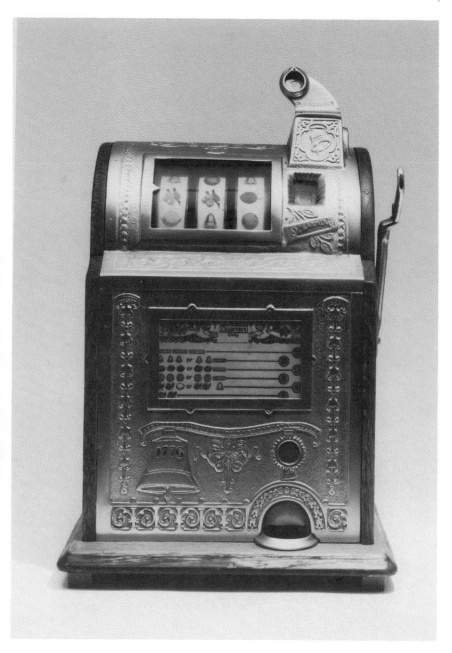

Watling 25¢ "Operator's Bell" Cast Iron Front Three-Reel Slot Machine, the wood sided machine with foliate and Liberty Bell cast decoration. 1920s, restored.
$5,000–7,000

Watling "Blue Seal" 5¢ Three-Reel Slot Machine, with twin jackpots, the front painted blue, yellow, and red. Circa 1920. H. 30". **$1,700–2,700**

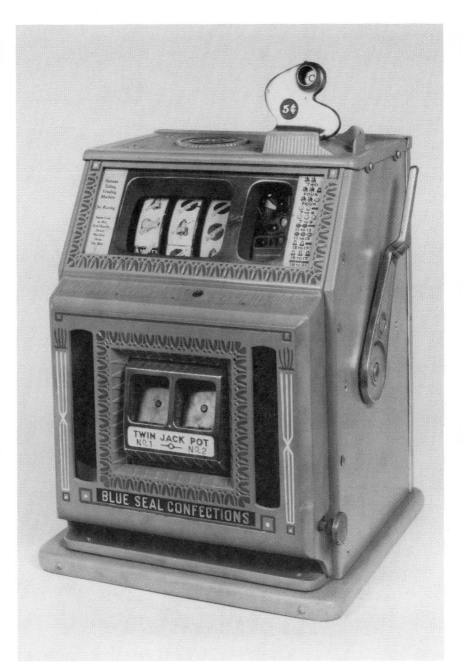

Watling "Blue Seal" 5¢ Three-Reel Slot Machine, with mint vendors, twin jackpots, and reels printed with fortunes across the traditional symbols. Circa 1931. H. 24½". **$1,900–2,800**

Watling Gooseneck 5¢ Three-Reel Slot Machine, with twin jackpot. Circa 1932.
H. 25".   **$1,500–2,500**

Watling "Blue Seal-2 Plays for 5¢" Three-Reel Slot Machine, with a twin jackpot. Circa 1932. H. 26". **$1,800-2,800**

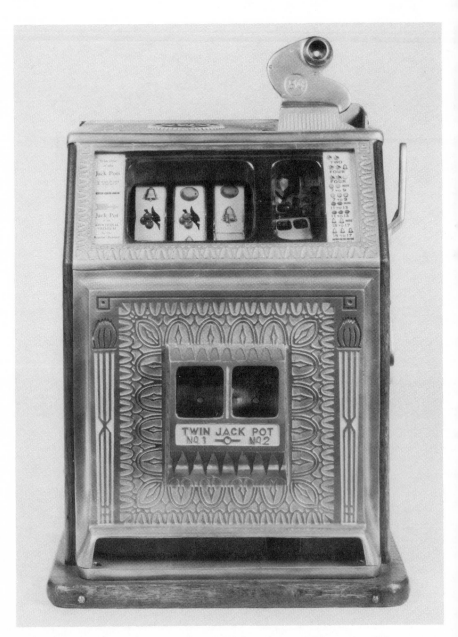

Watling 5¢ "Blue Seal" Three-Reel Slot Machine, with twin jackpots. Circa 1932. H. 24". **$1,500–2,500**

Watling "Blue Seal" 1¢ Three-Reel Slot Machine. This machine is rare in the 1c denomination. Mid-1930s, good original condition. H. 23¾" **$1,350–2,350**

Watling 5¢ "Rol-A-Top" Three-Reel Slot Machine, the front cast with coins cascading from a cornucopia with twin jackpots and fortune reel strips. Circa 1933. H. 28". **$3,200–4,700**

Watling "Rol-A-Top" 5¢ Three-Reel Slot Machine, the coin head and escalator in the form of a cornucopia spilling coins, with twin jackpots, the front detailed in red and yellow, complete with the original reel strips and award card. Circa 1935. H. 28". **$3,200–4,700**

A Watling "Cherry Front" Rol-A-Top 10¢ Three-Reel Slot Machine, the front cast with a silver cornucopia from which pour bright red cherries. Circa 1935, excellent restored condition. H. 26½". **$3,300–4,900**

Watling "Rol-A-Top" 5¢ Three-Reel Slot Machine, the top and front cast with coins cascading from a cornucopia, with twin jackpots. Circa 1935. H. 25".
$3,200–4,700

Watling 5¢ or 25¢ "Rol-A-Top" Three-Reel Slot Machine, the front cast with a cascade of cherries and accepting either nickels or quarters giving either one or five pulls, with twin and special jackpots. Circa 1935. H. 27". **$5,000–7,500**

Watling "Treasury" 5¢ Three-Reel Slot Machine, with twin jackpots, the front modeled with a gilt eagle and cascading coins. This machine is one of the most elaborately decorated ever produced. Circa 1935, H. 23½". **$4,200–5,750**

Watling "Treasury" 5¢ Three-Reel Slot Machine, the top and front cast with cascading coins, with twin jackpots. Circa 1936. H. 25½". **$4,200–5,750**

Watling 5¢ "Treasury", twin mint vendors and twin jackpots. Watling originally put this on the market as an inexpensive version of the Rol-A-Top. It wasn't as popular so not as many were made as the Rol-A-Top. The Treasury was the last gooseneck machine made by any manufacturer of slots. Produced between 1936 and 1941.   **$5,000–7,000**

Watling 5¢ "Rol-A-Top" Three-Reel Slot Machine, with twin jackpots, the front cast with cascading cherries with fortune reel strips. Circa 1936. H. 27"

$3,500–5,000

Watling "Treasury" 5¢ Three-Reel Slot Machine, with skills stops, the top and front cast with cascading coins, with twin jackpots. Circa 1936. H. 23".

$4,500–6,000

Watling "Treasury" 5¢ Three-Reel Slot Machine, the top and front cast with cascading coins, with twin jackpots, complete with the original award card and reel strips. Circa 1936. H. 25½". **$4,200–5,750**

Watling 5¢ "Rol-A-Top" Three-Reel Slot Machine, the gold-plated machine with Mills fortune reel strips and twin jackpots. Circa 1936, partially restored.

$3,200–4,700

Watling "Rol-A-Top" 25¢ Three-Reel Slot Machine with Conversion Castle-Front, the coin head and escalator in the form of a cornucopia spilling coins with twin jackpots, with a later conversion castle front applied in three sections. Circa 1941. H. 26". **$2,500–3,750**

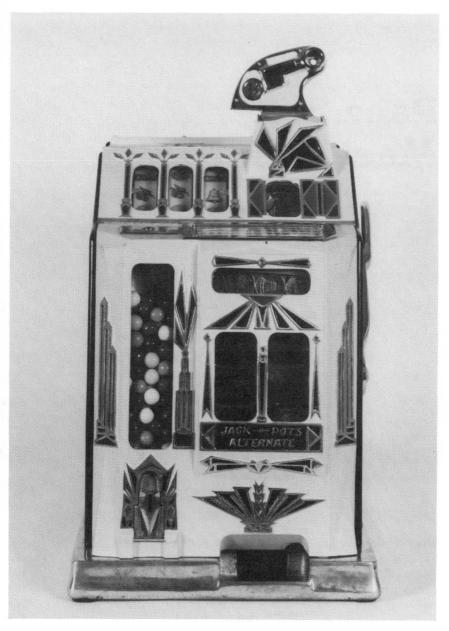

Superior 1¢ Confection Vendor, a gum ball vendor with gold award reel strips and original gold award tokens. This machine distributed by Superior, was made for the most part with Watling parts and contains the typical "tinny" Watling sound. Circa 1930, excellent restored with original reel strips and award card. H. 21½".
$4,500–5,500

Pace Slot
Machines

Operator Bell	1927	Kitty	1937
Jack-Pot	1928	Twin Bell	1938
Bantam Reserve	1930	Triple Bell	1938
Comet Vendor	1933	Saratoga Console	1939
Star	1933	Chrome Comet	1939
Races-Horserace	1934	Rocket	1939
Comet	1934	Club	1940
Comet Deferred Pay	1935	Reels	1941
Star Comet	1936	Century Console	1941
Gold Award	1936	Cherry	1945
Comet Console	1937	Silver Star	1945

Pace 5¢ Three-Reel Slot Machine. Circa 1928. H. 24".   **$1,550–2,550**

Pace "Bantam" 5¢ Three-Reel Slot Machine, the front with a mint vendor and a jackpot. Circa 1928. H. 19". **$1,750–2,750**

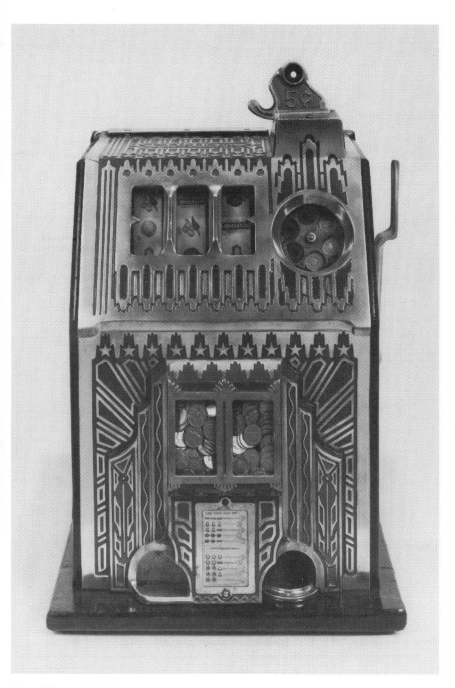

Pace "Comet" 5¢ Three-Reel Slot Machine, the front cast with starburst painted blue and red. Circa 1932. H. 26". **$1,500–2,500**

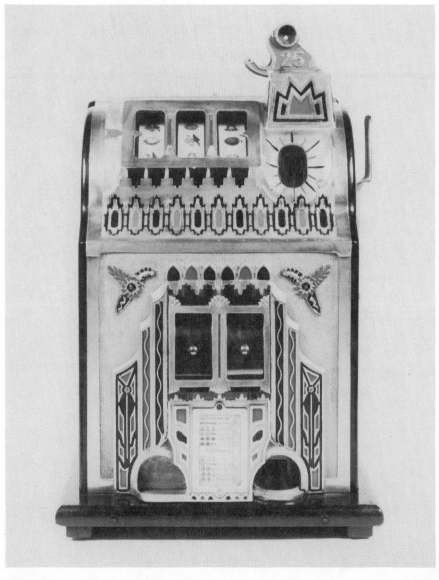

Pace 25¢ "Comet" Three-Reel Slot Machine, with a jackpot. Circa 1932.
H. 25".   **$1,600–2,600**

Pace 10¢ "Comet" Three-Reel Slot Machine, with a single jackpot. Circa 1932, good "original" condition. **$1,800–2,800**

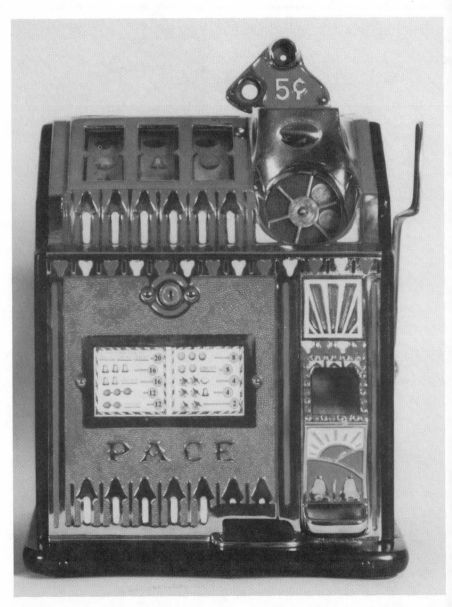

Pace "Bantam" 5¢ Three-Reel slot machine, three-quarter size. Circa 1933, excellent restored. H. 19". **$1,500–2,500**

Pace "Bantam" 5¢ Three-Reel Slot Machine, the front with mint vendor and jackpot. Circa 1935. H. 20". **$1,850–2,850**

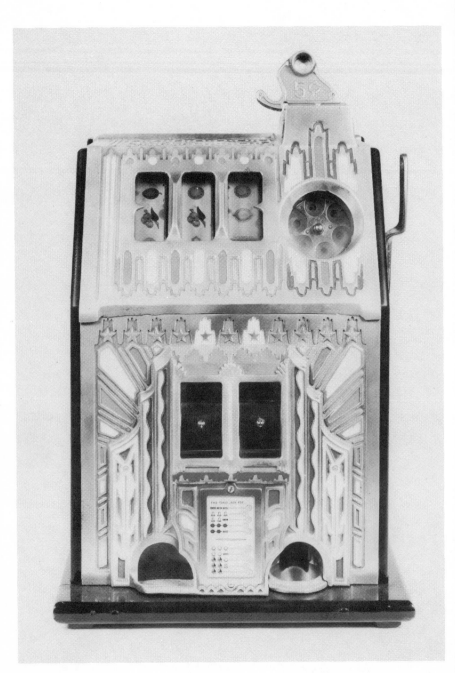

Pace 5¢ "Comet" Three-Reel Slot Machine, the front cast in Art Deco taste. Circa 1935. H. 24". **$1,200–2,200**

Pace "Bantam" 10¢ Three-Reel Slot Machine, the front cast with playing cards with a side vendor and front jackpot. Circa 1935. H. 24". **$1,500–2,500**

Pace "Bantam" 5¢ Three-Reel Slot Machine, with fortune reel strips and a jackpot. Circa 1935. H. 20".   **$1,500–2,500**

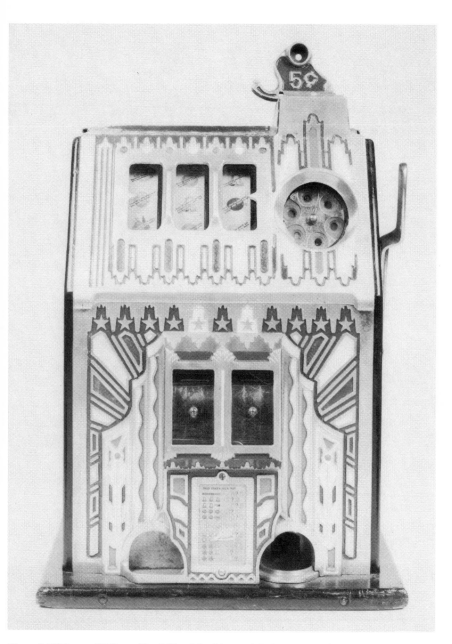

Pace 5¢ "Comet" Three-Reel Slot Machine, with fortune reel strips and jackpots.
Circa 1935. H. 25".   **$1,500–2,500**

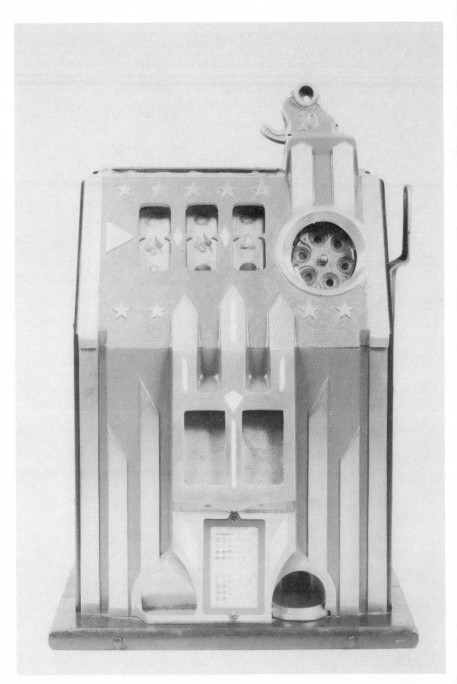

Pace "Comet" 10¢ Three-Reel Slot Machine. Circa 1935. H. 24". **$1,200–2,200**

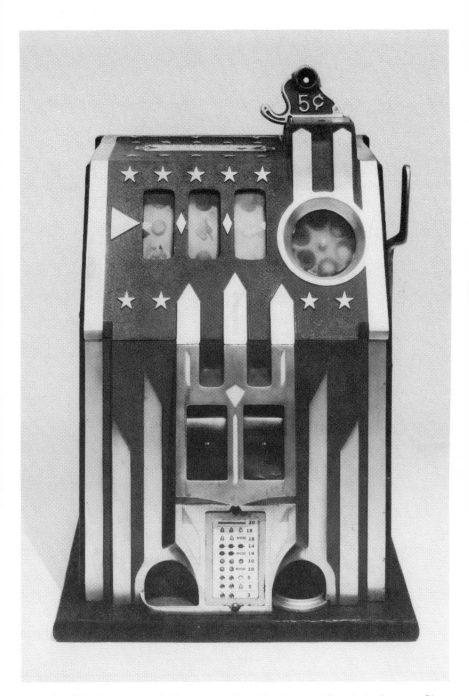

Pace 5¢ "All Star Comet" Three-Reel Slot Machine, with twin jackpots. Circa 1936, partially restored. **$1,200–2,200**

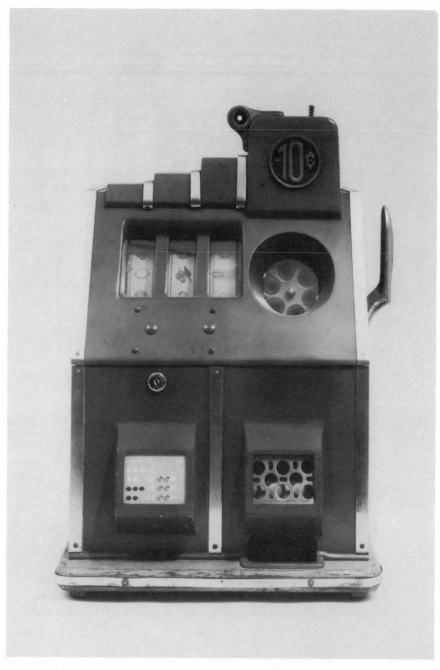

Pace 10¢ "Rocket" Three Reel Slot Machine, with single jackpot. *Circa 1936,*
good "original" condition. **$900–1,500**

Pace "8 Star Bell," a club model with a holder for a drink and an ashtray next to the coin payout cup. Variation of the 1940 Pace "Comet." **$1,000–1,750**

Caille Slot
Machines

CAILLE

Owl Upright	1897	Centaur Upright	1907
Detroit Upright	1898	Twin Upright	1907
Duck Upright	1898	Triple Upright	1907
Judge Upright	1899	Ben Hur Upright	1908
Duck Upright	1899	Liberty Bell	1909
Senator Upright	1899	Cast Iron Bell	1910
Star Upright	1899	Tourist Counter	1912
Puritan Upright	1900	Silver Cup	1912
Our Baby Counter Model	1901	Victory Bell	1920
Lion Upright	1901	Superior	1926
New Century Upright	1901	Superior Vendor	1927
Duck	1901	Superior Skill	1928
Cupid Upright	1902	Superior Jackpot	1929
Black Cat Upright	1902	Grand Prize	1930
Lone Star Upright	1902	Always Full	1931
Quaker Upright	1902	Reserve Jackpot	1931
Venus Upright	1902	Super Jackpot	1931
Victory Upright	1902	Silent Sphinx	1932
Forty-Five Upright	1903	Sphinx Ball Gum	1933
Seven Eleven Upright	1903	Gold Star	1933
Two Bits Upright	1903	New Deal	1933
Eclipse Upright	1904	Four Reel	1933
Twin Upright	1904	Jackpot Bell	1933
Triple Upright	1904	Ball Gum	1933
Big Six Upright	1904	Dictator	1934
Bull Frog Upright	1904	Little General	1934
New Gum Vendor Upright	1904	Dough Boy	1935
Roulette Floor Model	1904	Cadet	1936
Barbara Anne	1905	Commander	1937
Yankee Counter	1905	General	1937
Sun Upright	1907	Play Boy	1937
		Club Console	1937

Caille Brothers "Victory Bell" unusual center pull 25¢ Three-Reel Slot Machine, cast iron with double nude front, incorporating a circular window on the left side informing player of win or loss. The reel strips on this machine are considered to be the most graphically fine ever produced. Circa 1919, excellent restored. H. 26½". **$6,000–11,000**

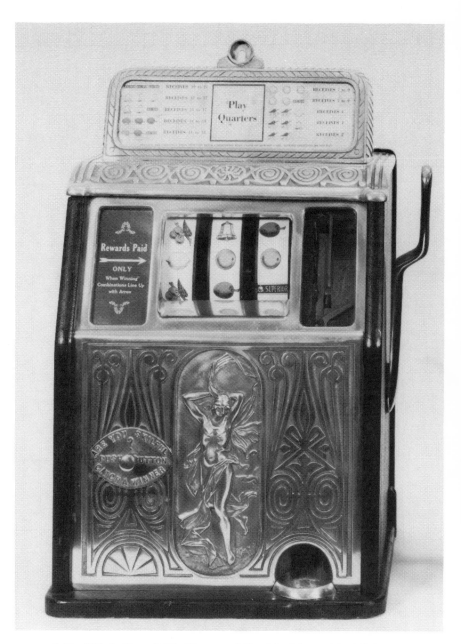

Caille "Nude Front" 25¢ Three-reel Slot Machine, with skill button. Skill buttons on any Caille machine are rare and especially so on a Caille "Nude". Circa 1929, good original condition. H. 22¼". **$2,500–4,000**

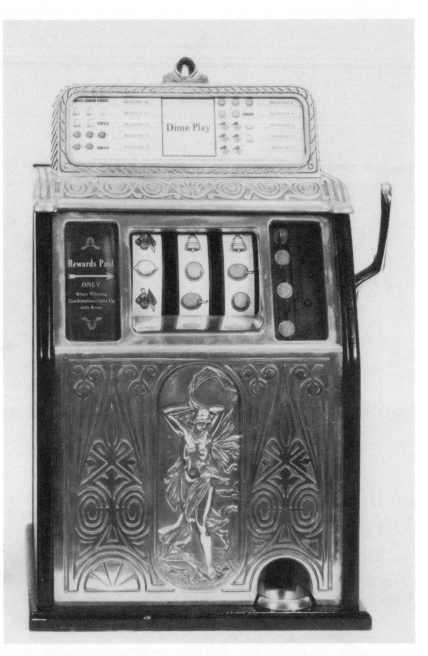

Caille "Nude Front" 10¢ Three-Reel Slot Machine, the case cast with a nude and intertwining spiral motifs. Circa 1930, good restored. H. 22½".
$2,000–3,750

Caille "Four Reel Superior" Slot Machine. Circa 1926. H. 24".   **$2,000–3,250**

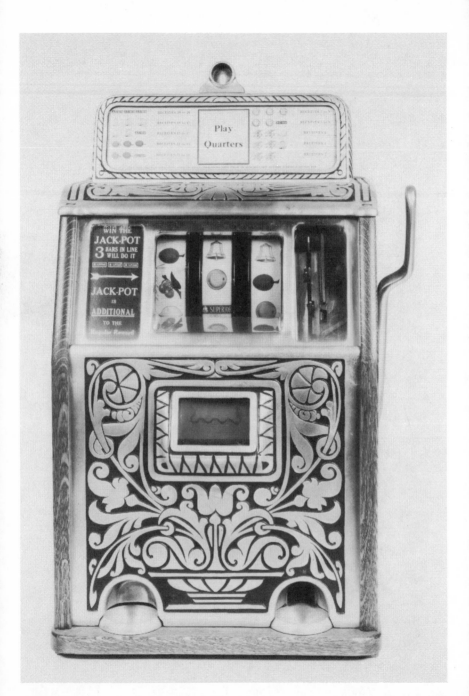

Caille 25¢ "Superior" Three-Reel Slot Machine, with a jackpot. Circa 1926.
H. 24".   **$1,500–2,500**

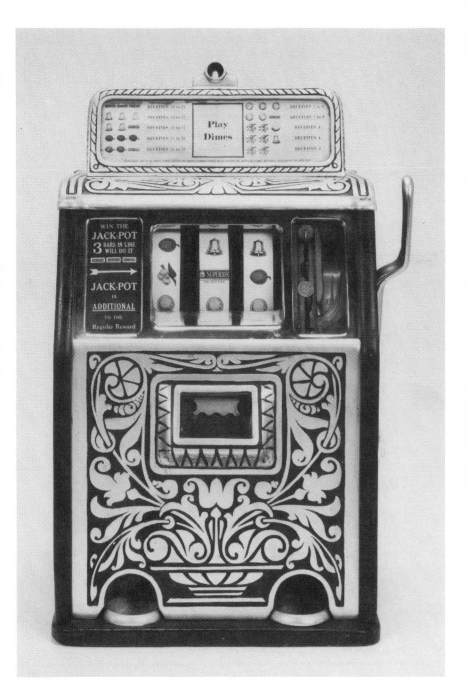

Caille "Superior Jackpot" 10¢ Three-Reel Slot Machine, the front cast with stylized foliage surrounding a jackpot. Circa 1928. H. 24½". **$1,500–2,500**

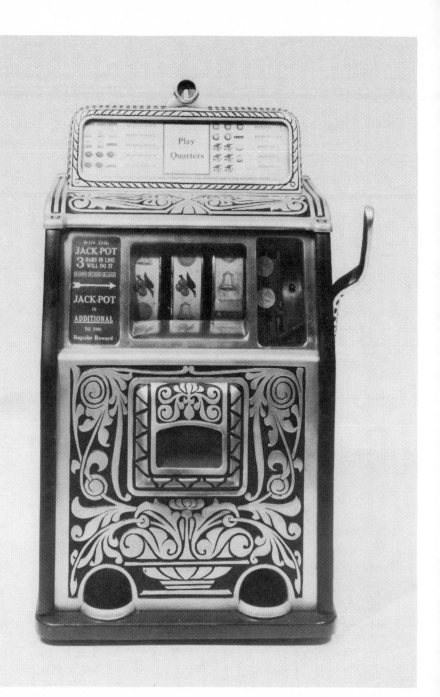

Caille 25¢ "Superior" Three-Reel Slot Machine, with single jackpot. Circa 1928, partially restored. **$1,500–2,500**

Caille 5¢ Silent "Sphinx" Three-Reel Slot Machine, with a double jackpot. Circa 1932, restored. H. 25". **$1,400–2,500**

Caille 10¢ Silent "Sphinx" Three-Real Slot Machine, with a jackpot. Circa 1932. H. 25". **$1,400–2,700**

Caille 10¢ "Doughboy" Three-Reel Slot Machine, equipped with a jackpot.
Circa 1936. H. 24". **$900–1,700**

Caille 5¢ "Playboy" Three-Reel Slot Machine, with jackpot. Circa 1936, partially restored. **$1,000–1,900**

Groetchen
Slot Machines

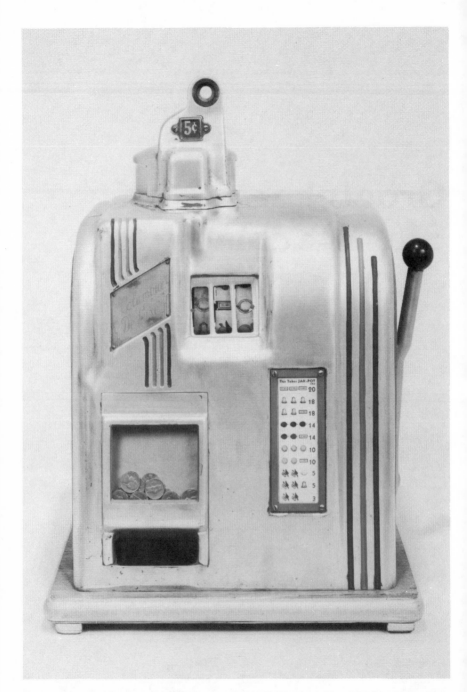

Groetchen Chrome "Columbia Deluxe" 5¢ Three-Reel Slot Machine, the front cast with red and blue-painted strips. Circa 1936. H. 23½". **$800–1,300**

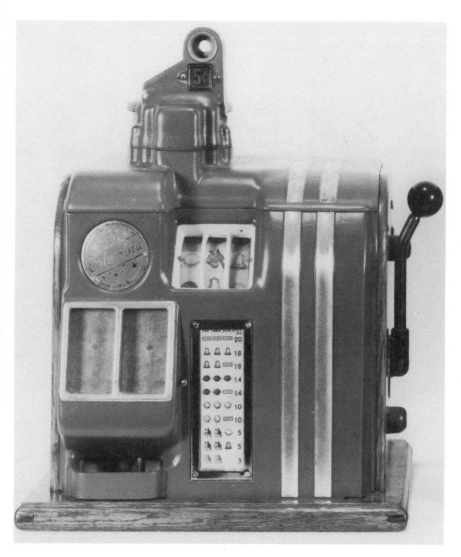

Groetchen "Columbia" 5¢ Three-Reel Miniature Slot Machine, with twin jackpots. 1930s, excellent restored. H. 18½". **$700–1,200**

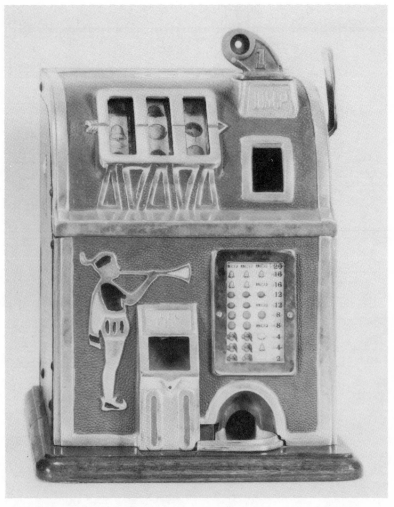

A Rare Benton Harbor "IMP" 1¢ Three-Reel Miniature Slot Machine, the front plate cast with a page blowing a hunting horn. Good restored. H. 17".
$1,800–2,800

Bally Slot
Machines

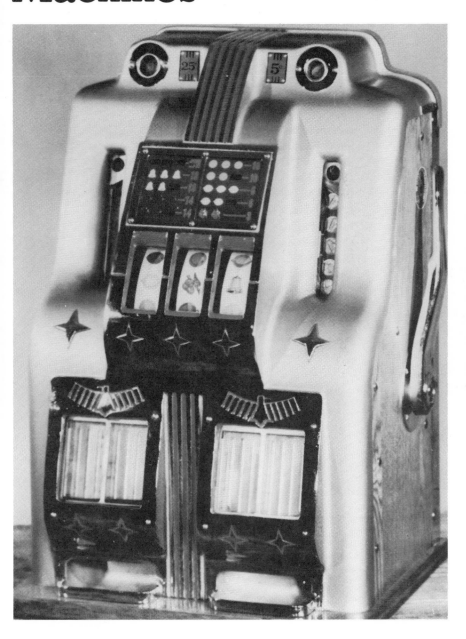

BALLY

Sparkplug Race	1934
Reliance Dice	1935
Super Flash Dice	1936
Race Track Console	1936
Double Bell	1938
Club Bell	1938
Lucky Double	1939
Jumbo Parade	1940
Club Bell Console	1941
Clover Bell	1941
Draw Bell Console	1946
Double Bell Console	1947
Triple Bell Console	1947
Wild Lemon	1948
Hi-Boy Console	1948

Bally 5¢ "Double Bell" Three-Reel Slot Machine, this model being the first type of slot machine produced by Bally Mfg. Co. Circa 1938. H. 28". **$1,550–2,750**

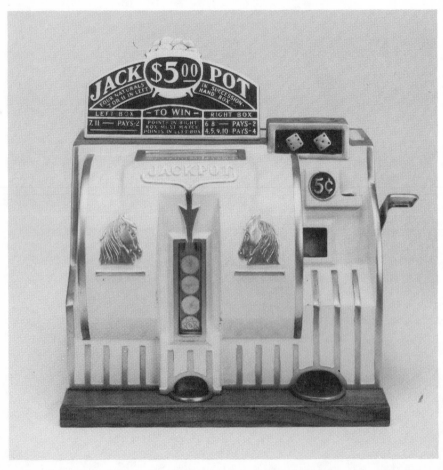

Bally "Reliance" 5¢ Dice Payout Machine, operating in the manner of a crap game, the yellow-painted front cast with horses' heads flanking a jackpot beneath a marquee. Circa 1936. H. 18". **$3,500–6,000**

QT, Miniature, and Bantam Slot Machines

Superior 5¢ "Midget" Two-Reel Slot Machine, with single jackpot. Circa 1932, fair "original" condition. **$1,750–2,750**

Benton Harbor 1¢ "Imp" Miniature Three-Reel Slot Machine. Circa 1932.
H. 18". $1,800–2,800

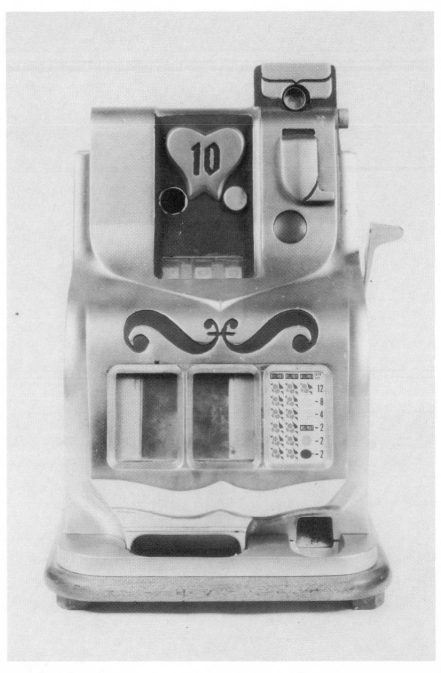

Mills 10¢ Chrome-Front "Q.T." Three-Reel Slot Machine, with twin jackpots. Circa 1934. H. 20". **$1,000–2,000**

Mills "Q.T." 5¢ Three-Reel Slot Machine, with twin jackpots. Circa 1934.
H. 20". **$900–1,750**

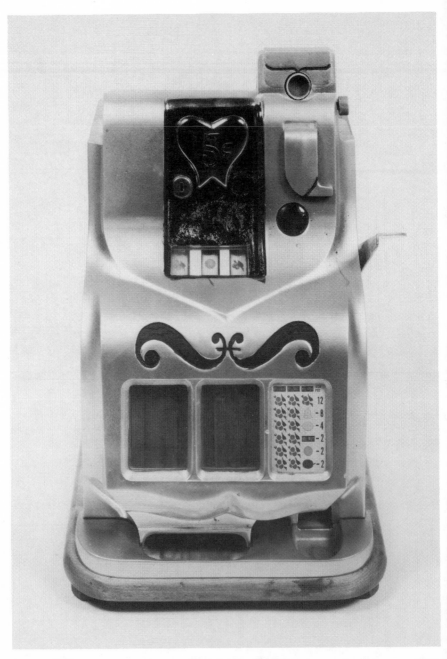

Mills Chrome-Front "Q.T." 5¢ Three-Reel Slot Machine, the front cast with scrolls, with twin jackpots complete with the original reel strips. Circa 1934. H. 20"   **$1,000–2,000**

Mills "Thunderbird Q.T." 1¢ Three-Reel Slot Machine, with rare bubble gum side vendor. Circa 1931, excellent restored. H. 18½". **$1,400–2,750**

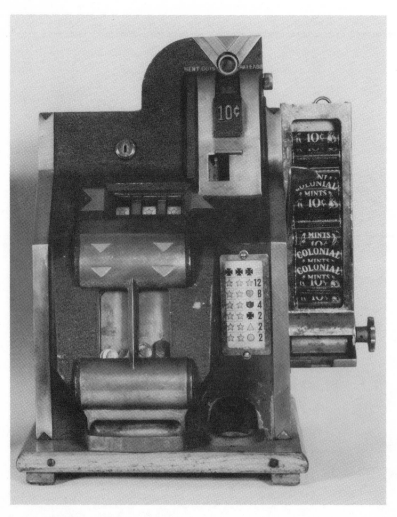

Mills "Q.T." 10¢ Three-Reel Slot Machine, with rare side mint vendor. Circa 1934, good original condition. H. 18½". **$1400-2,750**

Rare Watling 1¢ Bubble Gum Front Vendor Three-Reel Slot Machine, with original tin lithographed fortune telling reel strips. Mid-1930s, excellent restored. H. 23½". **$2,000–3,250**

Pace "Bantam" 1¢ Three-Reel Slot Machine, with original fortune telling reel strips, and rare bubble gum side vendor. 1930s, fine original condition. H. 20¼". **$1,750–3,000**

Mills "Q.T. Thunderbird" 5¢ Three-Reel Slot Machine, with chrome plated cast iron front and twin jackpots. Circa 1930, excellent restored. H. 18½".
$1,200–2,250

Mills "Q.T. Bell" machine, produced between 1934 and 1951. Very popular because of the small size and excellent mechanics. Light weight, 28 to 34 pounds. Produced in 1¢, 5¢, 10¢, and 25¢. The 25¢ machine is very rare. It was also made with gumball and mint vendor, gumball side vendor most desirable. Q T did not begin as shown here; the first model was a Q T Junior or Q T Silent, which is much rarer. Invented by Oscar Petersen, who worked for Mills Novelty Company. **$900–1,750**

Groetchen Blackjack Game 1¢ Gum Vendor, the cast aluminum front plate with five card windows. Circa 1934, good original condition. H. 15". **$800-1,000**

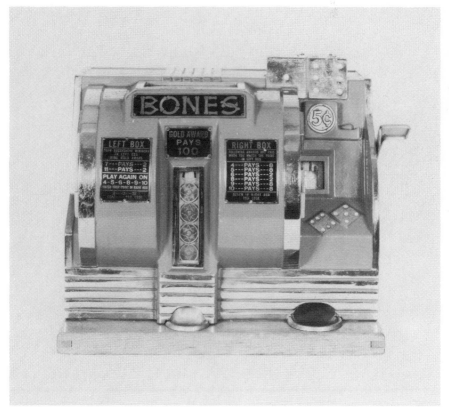

Buckley "Bones" 5¢ Dice Payout Gambling Machine, operating in the manner of a crap game, with award cards flanking a central jackpot. H. 13". Circa 1935.

$3,250–5,750

Mills "Vest Pocket" 5¢ Three Reel Slot Machine, a small metal case with a window at the top revealing the three reels, the payout covered with a hinged metal flap. Circa 1938. H. 8¼".   **$300–750**

Bally 5¢ "Reliance" Dice Payout Gambling Machine, operating in the manner of a crap game. Circa 1936. H. 18".   **$3,500–6,000**

A Vendet Midget 5¢ Two-Reel Slot Machine, the front plate cast with abstract designs. This two-reel machine is very rare. Circa 1935, excellent original condition. H. 15". **$2,000–3,250**

Western Hand-Carved Wood–Slot Machine Figures

I am sure we all agree that antique slot machines are beautiful examples of original American industrial art, but there is also a unique piece of true American folk art that incorporates a slot machine. These truly American works of art are called Polk carved figures.

These figures were carved by Mr. Frank Polk, a respected western artist and wood carver who specialized in cowboy art. Mr. Polk used real cowboys and other western characters as his models. He carved these figures for the Character Manufacturing Company of Nevada, from 1950 to 1952, who in turn sold them to various casinos in Reno and Las Vegas. Mr. Polk carved almost one hundred different western figures out of solid wood with a Mills Slot Machine in the figure's chest area. His most popular figure was, of course, the One-Armed Bandit. To my knowledge all of Mr. Polk's figures are now in private collections, except for one at the Golden Nugget, Las Vegas, Nevada. The hand carved figures rank with the wooden cigar store Indians that are sought after by investors and collectors alike.

In the late 1970s, a company called Royal Casino Antiques started to carve original western wooden figures, using an antique slot machine. Naturally these were compared to the Polk carved figures. They have become highly collectible and collectors and investors who already owned a Mills High-Top slot machine were eager to purchase one to make a complete statue. Again, the One-Armed Bandit is the most popular because it just goes so well with the slot machines.

I would venture to say that these newer figures will find their own value and market as the years go by for each one is different, an original designed in real wood and hand carved by an artist and painted by an artist. No one knows for how long these figures will be made and I believe that they are a good addition to any slot machine collection.

The prices of the Western Figure Collection are:

One-Armed Masked Bandit	*$4,500*
One-Armed Cowboy	*4,700*
Mexican Bandito	*6,100*
Miner	*4,900*
Indian	*5,900*

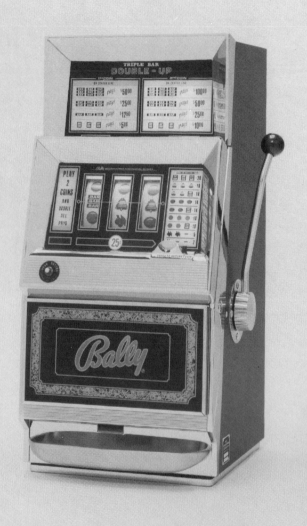

4. The Slot Machine Today

Bally Slot Data System III

You might wonder what has happened to the slot machine—in fact I don't know if any of the old timers would even recognize today's slot machine. The world's largest manufacturer, today, is Bally Manufacturing Corporation and while Bally still builds their slot machines in Chicago, Illinois, not far from the early factories of Pace, Jennings, Rock-Ola, Exhibit Supply, and Watling, their assembly line looks like it is turning out computers or jet aircrafts instead of slot machines.

Bally's production line uses the most modern, up-to-date, state of the art equipment to produce the most modern, up-to-date, trouble free slot machines in existence today. However, there are still many similarities today that were there in the very beginning; you still put your coin in the coin slot, pull the handle, watch the reels go round, and wait for them to stop, your eyes glued waiting for the cherries, bells, fruit, and bars to come to a stop so the machine can pass you your winnings. I am sure it is just as exciting as it ever was in the early 1900s when Charles Fey got together with Herbert Mills to manufacture the first real slot machine, the Mills "Liberty Bell," a good looking, reliable, and cheatproof machine. As if we pull the handle of a slot machine time machine we arrive in the 1980s to look at the Bally Slot Date Systems.

Bally has developed a system that is an on-line slot monitoring and accounting system, designed to provide maximum security and improve the efficiency and accuracy of all facets of casino slot operations. It utilizes the latest state of the art microprocessor technology to monitor, measure, record, and report all phases of slot activity from 10 to 2000 slot machines. I bet many an operator would have loved to have had a system like this available to them.

I will not attempt to go through the entire Bally System with you, but I will tell you it can and does do everything for the operator except put the coin into the machine.

The three basic components of the system are:

Communicator—A microprocessor based device designed and built by Bally, that mounts behind the handle of any slot machine and is wired directly to the machine's circuitry. The communicator's function is to constantly monitor all slot activity and send that information to the central processor.

Central Processor—This is a computer which polls each communicator sixteen times per second. Any information received is immediately analyzed by the computer.

Peripheral Terminals—These are terminals that let you check on the information from the central processor. One of its most important functions is the surveillance terminal that will alert you if there is a potential breach of security, actual attempts to cheat, or unauthorized entry of the slot or drop. As an option, Bally will provide a tie in to any surveillance camera system to automatically direct cameras to the slot where the problem has been detected while the action is still taking place.

Bally has also come out with a small system designed for as few as ten machines. In this system the Bally Game Storage Unit is safely mounted inside the slot machine and wired directly to the machine circuitry; the GSU assumes tamper-proof integrity of cash flow measurements.

If all this seems like Buck Rogers in the 25th Century all I can say is that it is!! I am glad I won't be here to see the new electric slot machines with all their computer and electronic gadgets of the future, and that is one reason that I like to play, fix, and just tinker with the beautiful old slot machines that we all know and love.

Some of Bally's innovations have been: Bally's "Bottomless" Payout Reserve, combining mechanical handle action, reel spin and stop with electrical circuitry.

Some Good Places and People to Contact for Slot Machines

I & J Concepts
P.O. Box 524
North Bellmore, New York
11710
Buy-Sell-Trade
• Highest Prices Paid •

Slot Machine Parts
Tom Krahl
238 Hecker Drive
Dundee, Illinois 60118

Back Pages Antiques
389 2nd Avenue
New York, New York 10010
Alan Luchnick

Vintage Machine Sales
1500 Adams
Costa Mesa, California 92626
Vinnie Dobos

G.A.M.E.S.
6626 Valjean Avenue
Van Nuys, California 91406

Gordon Pace
Pace Auctions
1591 Ellinwood Street
Des Plaines, Illinois 60016

Gill Shapiro
Urban Archaeology
137 Spring Street
New York, New York 10012

Charles McCann
Antique Coin Operated
    Vending Machines
P.O. Box 559
North Bellmore, New York 11710

Roy Arrington's
Victorian Casino
Antiques Auction
1421 So. Main Street
Las Vegas, Nevada 89104

Books on Gambling:
Gambler's Book Club
630 S. 11th Street
Box 4115
Las Vegas, Nevada 89106

Jim Davy
Newhall Pharmacy
24275 San Fernando Road
Newhall, California 91321

Books on How to Fix Slot Machines:
Coin Slot Books
Box 612
Wheatridge, Colorado 80033

Mark Schlesinger
Coin Operated Antiques

Collectors' Carrousel:

The best all-round marketplace for slot machines
and other coin-operated devices.

Watling "Treasury" 5¢ reel slot machine, circa 1936
(restored), height 25½ inches. Sold at our New York galleries
on August 1, 1980 for $5,250.00

Rare Caille "Puritan" 5¢ slot machine in an upright case,
with the original packing crate, height 64 inches. Sold at
our New York galleries on August 1, 1980 for $11,500.00

Mills 5¢ "Operators Bell" three-reel slot machine,
circa 1911, with a cast-iron case, height 25 inches. Sold
at our New York galleries on August 1, 1980 for $6,500.

Buyers and sellers both have come to appreciate
the marketing advantages of Sotheby's Collectors'
Carrousel auctions: handsomely illustrated
catalogues, pre-sale estimates, post-sale price lists
and exhibitions in the world's newest, most spacious
art auction gallery—Sotheby's York Avenue
Galleries.

Sellers especially benefit from the extensive
promotion, publicity and advertising each of our sales
receives. And out-of-town buyers enjoy the
convenience of bidding by order through our

Customer Advisory Service.

In fact, because we created Collectors' Carrousel
auctions just for fine collectibles, we can concentrate on
being the best slot machine marketplace around. For
information about buying and selling fine collectibles
at auction, please write or call Ms. Pamela Brown at
(212) 472-4783.

For an annual subscription to our Collectors'
Carrousel auctions, send a check for $35 to Sotheby's
Subscription Dept. PS, 980 Madison Avenue, New
York 10021.

Sotheby's
Founded 1744
Sotheby Parke Bernet Inc., 1334 York Avenue, New York 10021

⚜ The Original
Slot Machine for Dining

Horn & Hardart, once known almost exclusively for its "Automat," was referred to by many as the Restaurants That Nickels Built. That statement could also be true today since Horn & Hardart is now in the gaming business with its recently acquired ROYAL AMERICANA Hotel & Casino, located in Las Vegas, Nevada. This facility is currently being remodeled and expanded to include a keynote addition of a new Horn & Hardart Automat "the original slot machine for dining."

A young man named Joe Horn with $1,000 to his name teamed up with a lunchroom waiter named Hardart and launched the world's most successful restaurant venture — a phenominal operation that grossed 71 million dollars in 1954 and has made "Automat" part of our language! It all started in 1888 as a hole in the wall lunchroom in Philadelphia serving the best coffee in town. During the 1950's the company had 36 restaurants in Philadelphia and 45 in New York feeding some 800,000 people a day. The Automat fan put a nickel in a slot and threw the lever and through the mouth of a chrome dolphin's head gushed the right amount of the right coffee at the right temperature and with the right amount of cream mixed with it. The magic symbolism of the dolphin's head and that of other mechanical dispensers of various hot and cold dishes, caused customers, especially those in New York to refer to the restaurants collectively as "The Automat."

One of the reasons for success at Horn & Hardart was that they only used the highest grade, and hence the costliest of raw materials going into their food. Their quality was unsurpassed; everything was always fresh and no food was kept overnight. The rapid turnover of the many people they fed insured freshness.

I remember, as a child, my father taking me to an Automat in New York and giving a change girl $1.00. She would throw down the nickels without counting them and never ever made a mistake. There were always 20 for $1.00. We would take these nickels to the bank of coin operated machines that were operated by putting in the coins and turning the handle. The glass door would snap open and you could take out your food.

For over 60 years Horn & Hardart basically remained unchanged, the change has been rapid in the last 10 years. Today it is a diversified company operating in three industries — Food Service, Mail Order and Hospitality and Gaming.

The Food Service is basically centered in New York and Florida consisting principally of Burger King and Arby's fast food franchised restaurants. It has also kept two Horn & Hardart small automat cafeterias and some other restaurants.

Their Mail Order Division known as Hanover House Industries is a recognized leader in the world and through its 12 catalog divisions specialize in merchandise designed and chosen to appeal to all ages, lifestyles and income levels. Catalogs are created to present merchandise tailor made for those various population segments, recognizing their needs and interests.

Their Hospitality and Gaming Division is their newest and also I believe their most exciting. It is operated by Alan Maiss who is President of Royal Center, Inc., a wholly owned subsidiary which operates the company's Royal Americana Hotel & Casino in Las Vegas, Nevada. It is a very centrally located and exciting Hotel Casino which has currently been remodeled to make it one of the most modern and appealing of all Las Vegas casinos.

Besides the new Horn & Hardart Automat which they have built, it also includes a restaurant featuring char-broiled exhibition cooking, which is unique to Las Vegas.

The inserting of coins for one to purchase a piece of cherry pie has now evolved into inserting coins into the slot machines; however, the customer is still looking for the payoff of the jackpot when the cherries come up.

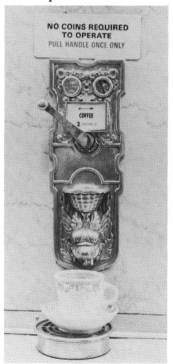

The original slot machine.

An old Automat in New York.

A wall of food slot machines.

Abbott & Costello at the Automat.

Alan Maiss, President of Royal Center, Inc., a wholly owned subsidiary of Horn & Hardart which operates the company's Royal Americana Hotel & Casino in Las Vegas, Nevada, standing next to the latest state of the art Bally slot machine on the floor of the casino.

Here's how to get your FREE copy of the "Slot Machine Newsletter":

This entitles the bearer to a free copy of the "Slot Machine Newsletter." Published by the authors of this book to foster interest in antique slot machine collecting.

Name _____

Address _____

City _____

State _____ Zip _____

Send completed form to:
NEWSLETTERS
P.O. Box 524
North Bellmore, N.Y. 11710

About the Authors

Richard D. and Barbara Reddock have been collecting advertising and American collectibles for many years and have found it to be a most happy and rewarding experience.

The Reddocks became interested in antique slot machines in September, 1979 when the New York State Legislature passed Bill #(687-A) which allowed individuals to own antique slot machines.

Richard D. Reddock is an investment executive with Shearson Loeb Rhoades Inc., in Garden City, New York. Mr. Reddock is listed in *Who's Who in Business and Finance*.

Barbara Reddock is also an investment executive and a member of the President's Club with Shearson Loeb Rhoades. She is the mother of two children, Jill Beth, 11, and Ian, 13. Barbara is also a consultant and decorator on *Advertising American*.

The Reddocks are also the authors of *Planters Peant Advertising & Collectibles*.